How to Hear Police, Fire, and Aircraft Radio

by Len Buckwalter

HOWARD W. SAMS & CO., INC.
THE BOBBS-MERRILL CO., INC.
INDIANAPOLIS · KANSAS CITY · NEW YORK

FIRST EDITION

SECOND PRINTING—1971

International Standard Book Number: 0-672-20781-8
Library of Congress Catalog Card Number: 76-118367

Preface

Old radios often boast of bands that excite the listener with a promise of police calls, fire alarms, and aircraft communications. But try to tune these transmissions on a radio which extends only to 30 MHz, and you will probably be greeted by static or silence. The explosive growth in communications has driven these services far beyond the conventional short-wave bands. Where did they go?

If you were able to tune a TV receiver just below Channel 2, you might pick up your local police department at about 45 MHz. Tune an entertainment-type fm radio above the highest point on the dial (108 MHz) and you would start to hear aircraft navigational stations. The voices of pilots and ground controllers will be found slightly higher on the band. Two-way radios devoted to public safety communication, including police and fire calls, will be found in a band that lies between TV channels 6 and 7.

Since police, fire, and aircraft stations are now sprinkled over many bands and frequencies, finding the ones you might want to hear is no longer a simple task. It takes a combination of technical knowledge, planning, and some detective work, which is why this book was written.

The author wishes to thank his wife, Nancy, whose assistance proved invaluable.

LEN BUCKWALTER

Contents

1

A World of Shorter Waves

In the middle of the night, I was once awakened by a siren. It was unusual because sounds in the night ordinarily rise and fall unnoticed. This time, however, the siren sounded as if a fire truck were about to rumble up the driveway. A glance out the window quickly showed why: the sky nearby was illuminated with a red glow. Just below treetop level was an area of bright yellow flame. Was it a forest fire, possibly a threat to my house?

I reached for a small portable radio, extended the whip antenna and tuned the dial to a frequency of 34.86 MHz. An earphone was plugged into the set so the sound would not disturb sleeping members of the family. I listened, and within minutes, I had the facts by monitoring two-way radio communications. I learned exactly where the fire was—a nearby neighbor's home. A large part of the house had already been destroyed, but the family had been evacuated and there was no threat to the adjacent area. Finally, voices on the radio reported that the blaze was under control.

I heard this reassuring information by tuning to the operating frequency of the local volunteer fire department. The receiver could simultaneously pick up fire units at the scene, vehicles en route to the conflagration, and the dispatcher back at the fire house. It was little more than a transistor portable, but, in addition to the regular a-m broadcast band, it could also tune a band which extends from 30 to 50 MHz.

This is the beginning of a world of shorter waves. It is the start of the vhf (very high frequency) band, which contains the major frequency allocations for police, fire, and aircraft communications.

THE VHF BAND

Covering a range of 30 to 300 MHz, the vhf band begins where most shortwave receivers leave off. The conventional shortwave band ends at 30 MHz, which effectively excludes the most important two-way radio frequencies. On the short-wave band, you cannot tune the some 20,000 stations engaged in police communications, about 15,000 fire depart-

Fig. 1-1. Airport control tower at Reading, Pennsylvania.

ments, and approximately 200,000 aviation-connected stations (Fig. 1-1).

Although vhf bears most of the "public-safety" and aircraft communications, it is supplemented by one other band. It is the uhf (ultrahigh frequency) band, running from 300 to 3000 MHz. With a slice from 450 to 470 MHz set aside for two-way radio, the uhf band contains the frequency space needed to take up the expanding volume of mobile radio communications. In this book, however, the emphasis will be on vhf, the mainstay of police, fire, and aircraft radio in terms of equipment and operating activity.

It was not until the 1960's that practical equipment became available for monitoring these frequencies in the home or car. Prior to that time, virtually all circuits consisted of tube-type equipment in the high-cost industrial, commercial, or government category. The breakthrough arrived with transistors. First, they replaced audio stages in receivers, and, as technology improved, they supplanted tubes in the critical higher-frequency stages. Costs dropped, as the price of high-frequency transistors plummeted in a few short years. This opened the way for a remarkable variety of communications receivers at prices more commonly attached to entertainment-type sets.

Another appeal of vhf communications is in the antenna. Since wavelengths on the vhf band are physically quite short, the antennas used to pick them up are also small (Fig. 1-2). Much listening is possible with the telescoping whip antenna built into many sets. In many locations, a short length of ordinary wire serves the purpose. Unlike conventional shortwave listening over oceans, monitoring the higher bands is often done at short distances from the transmitting point. Local signals are usually strong enough for good reception without an elaborate antenna system. If the listener wants to pull in stations from greater distances, there are, as we will see later, many techniques and antennas available for the purpose.

Combining the features of low-cost equipment, solid-state circuits, and modest antenna, you have a medium which is

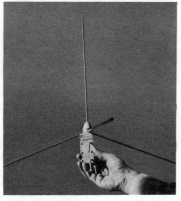

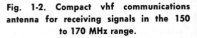

Fig. 1-2. Compact vhf communications antenna for receiving signals in the 150 to 170 MHz range.

Fig. 1-3. Mobile monitor mounted below regular car radio.

convenient to acquire and use. Listening can be done almost anywhere and at any time—in the home, on the highway (Fig. 1-3), or even while on foot with a portable.

WHY LISTEN

These bands are monitored for a variety of reasons. The earliest purchasers of vhf equipment had some professional or business reason for listening. For example, visit an airport and peer into a back office. You might see a special receiver on a shelf tuned to the aircraft band. Although office personnel may not be able to talk through the communications system, they can monitor on-the-air activity which affects their business. This brand of monitoring extends to the volunteer fireman, the off-duty policeman, and the pilot. A monitoring receiver keeps the professional informed about situations that might demand his attention.

Another group of listeners acquires this equipment because it can keep them posted on emergency conditions in their area. That fire described in the beginning of this chapter is one example. When a natural or man-made disaster strikes, public-safety officials use two-way radio to expedite rescue or assistance.

Another group consists of the casual shortwave listeners (SWL). They may have no particular stake in what is happening on the air, but wish to tune in because it is interesting, and often exciting, listening. There is always the lure of hearing some cliff-hanging emergency, like the one shown in Fig. 1-4, when the radio crackles with activity.

Fig. 1-4. An emergency, like this aircraft ditching, may be monitored on the vhf band.

SAMPLING THE BANDS

Monitoring two-way radio is not like listening to standard-broadcast or international-shortwave radio. These broadcast services are continuous, and you usually listen for sustained periods. However, two-way radio is in the category of "communications," where transmissions are brief, sporadic, and unpredictable. You will rarely hear transmissions which last more than a few seconds or minutes. You may hear a dispatcher speaking almost continuously, but he is actually addressing brief phrases to many different outlying mobile units. You may not even hear many of the mobile units because the vehicles travel behind hills or other obstructions which reduce the range. For these reasons, monitoring may not command your full attention. It is usually done with the receiver in the background, while the listener is attending some other activity. When the loud-speaker comes to life, you start listening.

Tuning in police frequencies usually brings a degree of activity keyed to the local population. For example, if you monitor the police frequency in a town of about 15,000, you may hear a few brief transmissions each day. In a larger city, a police dispatcher speaks almost continuously. He will be sending cars to the scenes of crimes, accidents, or other events (Fig. 1-5). You may hear of hijacked trucks, prowlers, stolen cars, burglaries, and medical emergencies. Police departments often use codes for radio transmissions. The popular "10" code is given in Chart 1-1.

Fire frequencies usually become active only during an alarm. There may be less overall activity than on other frequencies, but you can usually follow the operations in some detail when the local department responds to a call. As in other services, a fire department may have radio units in cars and trucks, as well as walkie-talkies for on-the-scene reports by men on foot.

Aircraft radio has a special fascination, but it takes some decoding to understand. You will often hear aircraft in flight more than 100 miles away because a high antenna position provides excellent range. However, you may hear only one side of a conversation, since aircraft rarely talk to each other, but mostly maintain communications with the ground. Stations on the ground include towers, FAA flight-service stations, and air-traffic control. Do not expect to monitor the ground stations unless you are within about 15 or 20 miles of an airport. Ground stations easily communicate with aircraft in flight, but their low power quickly dissipates over a ground path.

Airline captains are often heard reporting position, altitude, and headings to air-traffic control stations. The system

Fig. 1-5. Policeman using walkie-talkie
on vhf band.

Chart 1-1. "10" Code Used by Law-Enforcement Agencies

10-0 —Caution
10-1 —Unable copy—change location
10-2 —Signal good
10-3 —Stop transmitting
10-4 —Acknowledge (OK)
10-5 —Relay
10-6 —Busy—unless urgent
10-7 —Out of service
10-8 —In service
10-9 —Repeat
10-10—Fight in progress
10-11—Dog case
10-12—Stand by (stop)
10-13—Weather—road report
10-14—Prowler report
10-15—Civil disturbance
10-16—Domestic problem
10-17—Meet complainant
10-18—Quickly
10-19—Return to ....
10-20—Location
10-21—Call ...... by telephone
10-22—Disregard
10-23—Arrived at scene
10-24—Assignment completed
10-25—Report in person (meet) ....
10-26—Detaining subject, expedite
10-27—(Drivers) license information
10-28—Vehicle registration information
10-29—Check for wanted
10-30—Unnecessary use of radio
10-31—Crime in progress
10-32—Man with gun
10-33—EMERGENCY
10-34—Riot
10-35—Major crime alert
10-36—Correct time

10-37—(Investigate) suspicious vehicle
10-38—Stopping suspicious vehicle
10-39—Urgent—use light, siren
10-40—Silent run—no light, siren
10-41—Beginning tour of duty
10-42—Ending tour of duty
10-43—Information
10-44—Permission to leave .... for ....
10-45—Animal carcass at ....
10-46—Assist motorist
10-47—Emergency road repair at ....
10-48—Traffic standard repair at ....
10-49—Traffic light out at ....
10-50—Accident (F, PI, PD)
10-51—Wrecker needed
10-52—Ambulance needed
10-53—Road blocked at ..
10-54—Livestock on highway
10-55—Intoxicated driver
10-56—Intoxicated pedestrian
10-57—Hit and run (F, PI, PD)
10-58—Direct traffic
10-59—Convoy or escort
10-60—Squad in vicinity
10-61—Personnel in area
10-62—Reply to message
10-63—Prepare make written copy
10-64—Message for local delivery
10-65—Net message assignment
10-66—Message cancellation

10-67—Clear for net message
10-68—Dispatch information
10-69—Message received
10-70—Fire alarm
10-71—Advise nature of fire
10-72—Report progress on fire
10-73—Smoke report
10-74—Negative
10-75—In contact with . . .
10-76—En route ....
10-77—ETA (Estimated Time Arrival)
10-78—Need assistance
10-79—Notify coroner
10-80—Chase in progress
10-81—Breatherlizer report
10-82—Reserve lodging
10-83—Work school xing at ......
10-84—If meeting ..... advise ETA
10-85—Delayed due to . . .
10-86—Officer/operator on duty
10-87—Pickup/distribute checks
10-88—Present telephone # of ......
10-89—Bomb threat
10-90—Bank alarm at . . .
10-91—Pick up prisoner/ subject
10-92—Improperly parked vehicle
10-93—Blockade
10-94—Drag racing
10-95—Prisoner/subject in custody
10-96—Mental subject
10-97—Check (test) signal
10-98—Prison/jail break
10-99—Wanted/stolen indicated

provides safe separation between aircraft operating under low visibility (instrument conditions). Sometimes you will hear FAA pilots reporting the performance of radio equipment. The federal agency regularly checks the accuracy of the radio navigation aids that form the airways of the nation. Also, many small airports operate a "unicom" channel for communicating with small planes. It is used mainly to advise private pilots on runway and wind conditions.

Some of the most interesting aircraft listening can be done near an airport control tower. With either a mobile receiver or a portable carried outdoors, you may see and hear the traffic flow in and out of the airport. The tower is heard controlling aircraft approaching to land or taking off. With some careful listening, you will be able to visually pick out specific airplanes responding to instructions. Tune to another frequency and you will hear the ground controller guiding aircraft movements on the ground. He will transmit taxiing instructions, and guide the airplane to the proper runway for take off. It is something like watching a huge chess game, while hearing a running radio commentary.

The aircraft band sometimes sounds an emergency. Pilots may become lost, experience engine failure, run out of fuel, or experience bad-weather problems. Emergency calls, though infrequent, can be monitored on an emergency channel and on aircraft frequencies detailed in a later chapter.

OTHER SERVICES

Aviation does not share its slice of the vhf spectrum. You hear only communications associated in some way with the operation of aircraft. This is not true for the spectrum allocated to police and fire radio. There is considerable sharing with other services, as shown in Fig. 1-6. You will hear a multitude of other communications on receivers purchased for police and fire monitoring. (Some sets say "Police," for example, but still receive these other stations.) Chart 1-2 shows how they are grouped by the Federal Communications Commission (FCC) under such categories as Industrial, Land Transportation, and Public Safety. It is the Public Safety group that contains police and fire radio, as well as local government, highway maintenance, forestry conserva-

Chart 1-2. Major 2-Way Radio Services

Aviation	Aircraft group
	Aeronautical and fixed group
	Aviation auxiliary group
	Aviation radionavigation land
	Civil Air Patrol
Marine	Ship group
	Coastal group
	Marine auxiliary group
	Marine radar land
	Alaskan group
Public Safety	Police
	Fire
	Local government
	Highway maintenance
	Forestry conservation
	Special emergency
	State guard
Industrial	Special industrial
	Business
	Power
	Petroleum
	Manufacturers
	Forest products
	Industrial radiolocation
	Motion picture
	Relay press
	Telephone maintenance
Land Transportation	Railroad
	Taxicab
	Automobile emergency
	Interurban passenger (motor carrier)
	Interurban property (motor carrier)
	Urban passenger (motor carrier)
	Urban property (motor carrier)
Amateur & Disaster	Citizens
	Amateur
	RACES
	Disaster

tion, state guard, and special emergency services. The Industrial group offers channels to almost every type of private business. Certain organizations are given priority assignments because they provide special services. Utility companies, for example, have the Power Radio Service, and the oil and gas industry has the Petroleum Radio Service. For manufacturers, there is the Manufacturers Radio Service. The Business Radio Service takes care of almost anyone else who requires two-way radio. The last major category —Land Transportation—covers truckers, railroads, taxi-cabs, and emergency services for motorists. Thus, while you are tuning for police or fire calls,you will hear a significant amount of other traffic in the same frequency range.

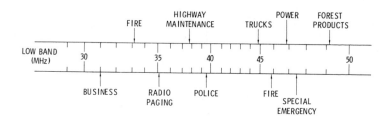

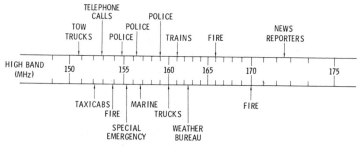

Fig. 1-6. Vhf bands are shared by many radio services.

THE LEGAL QUESTION

"Is it legal to listen to police and other radio services?" is a question that naturally arises. The answer, in most cases, is yes, with certain exceptions. You will not need a special permit or license from the FCC to purchase receiving equipment. The Federal Communications Commission concerns itself primarily with transmitting equipment and has few regulations dealing with receivers. The sale of receivers to the public is generally unlimited.

There is one important rule which should be known by anyone planning to receive two-way radio signals. There is a federal regulation generally termed "secrecy of communications" which states that you may not divulge the content of any communication you hear to another person, or use the information for your own benefit. In addition to this federal ruling, some states have passed regulations which forbid the use of police monitoring equipment in automobiles. If you want to install a mobile set, check first to see if any local restriction is in force. If so, you will have to confine your listening to the home. Even where the local government forbids reception in a car, the same restriction should not extend to monitoring while in your own home.

2

Bands and Frequencies

Two-way communications operate on several bands within the radio spectrum. The listener needs to know the frequency of the service he wishes to hear in order to choose the right equipment and tune the desired frequency. Although some sets can pick up several bands, no single receiver tunes every possibility. So let us consider how the bands are set up for the various services, and how you can find their location on the dial.

CHOOSING THE CORRECT BAND

Since the term "band" is used loosely in two-way radio, let us examine it closely. In its general meaning, a "band" is the frequencies, within given limits, which tend to behave the same way. The vhf (very high frequency) band, for example, contains radio waves which travel line of sight, with little bending around the curvature of the earth. The vlf (very low frequency) band suggests signals which easily travel along the ground, and even penetrate water. As formulated through international agreements, the major bands are shown in complete form in Table 2-1. The expression kHz indicates 1000 cycles, MHz is 1,000,000 cycles, and GHz means 1,000,000,000 cycles. You can see that there are eight major divisions. Below the lowest band (vlf), are the frequencies of sound, and beyond the highest band (ehf), a

Table 2-1. Major Bands in the Radio Spectrum

Band	Frequency Range
VLF (very low frequency)	Below 30 kHz
LF (low frequency)	30 to 300 kHz
MF (medium frequency)	300 to 3000 kHz
HF (high frequency)	3 to 30 MHz
VHF (very high frequency)	30 to 300 MHz
UHF (ultrahigh frequency)	300 to 3000 MHz
SHF (superhigh frequency)	3 to 30 GHz
EHF (extremely high frequency)	30 to 300 GHz

signal would assume the character of a light wave. Between these extremes are the bands we want to monitor.

Most police, fire, and aircraft radios operate in the vhf band, which extends from 30 to 300 MHz. This was not always the case. Prior to World War II, most services were jammed into the relatively narrow bands below 30 MHz. But as the demand for channels grew, and engineers produced practical equipment for higher frequencies, the vhf band opened for two-way radio. This explains why an old short-wave receiver may be marked to receive police calls, but not be able to pick up any signals. In earlier days, the public-safety stations were technically compelled to operate on lower bands.

There are occasional exceptions. When a service requires long-range communications beyond the horizon, it receives allocations on the high-frequency (hf) band below 30 MHz. One example is aviation. The aircraft band is on vhf for most continental operations, but airplanes can switch to lower channels when engaged in extended flight over water. The hf band provides long-distance communications via "skip" signals through the ionosphere. An aircraft crossing an ocean can choose among many 3 to 30 MHz channels and can communicate over distances of 1000 miles or more. This is in contrast to vhf, which is generally limited to about 200 miles, even when used at high altitude (above 30,000 feet) by jet transports. If you want to monitor intercontinental aviation, you can do it on a conventional short-wave receiver with continuous coverage from the standard a-m band through 30 MHz. In this book, however, we will concentrate on the spectrum above the high-frequency band, where most of the activity is concentrated.

Vhf is not the only band for police, fire, and aircraft radio. These services also are assigned in the uhf (ultra-high frequency) band. Two-way communications continuously grow and are forced to move to higher frequencies where there is additional space. The public-service assignments in the uhf band are from 450 to 470 MHz. The vhf band, however, is the most active and spacious band for two-way communications.

If we look closely at the vhf band, we discover that it is sliced into smaller segments, as shown in Fig. 2-1. Note that TV channels 2 through 6 occupy a large chunk of the vhf band from 54 to 88 MHz. A small section from 88 to 108 MHz, is devoted to fm broadcasting. The remaining vhf TV channels (7 through 13) are located from 174 to 214 MHz on the band. The vhf band is also spotted with several amateur (ham) frequency allocations at 50, 144, and 220 MHz.

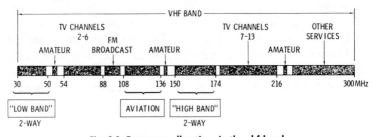

Fig. 2-1. Frequency allocations in the vhf band.

LOW-BAND VHF

The first segment of the vhf band for police and fire radio is called the "low band." This is because it is situated at the lower end of the vhf band from 30 to 50 MHz. It is also the oldest of the vhf bands, since expansion has been in the upward direction. The low band is not used exclusively for police and fire departments, but is shared with other services. Police and fire departments, however, are usually situated within certain portions of the band. As shown in Fig. 2-2, police frequencies may be assigned from about 37 to 46 MHz, while fire frequencies tend to be grouped within the 33 to 46.5 MHz slot. A common practice is to assign the

Fig. 2-2. Police and fire frequency assignments on low-band vhf.

same channel to several towns in the same general area. (The terms "frequency" and "channel" are used interchangeably. They refer to an exact point on the dial or band.)

HIGH-BAND VHF

Many police and fire departments in large cities operate on the "high band" in the upper vhf band. The band, which covers a frequency range of approximately 150 to 174 MHz, is similarly shared with other radio services. Police and fire assignments are concentrated in the frequency segments shown in Fig. 2-3.

Regardless of which band is used in a particular community, police and fire services are assigned specific channels. When the city or area is densely populated, there are usually several channel allocations. (The New York City police department, for example, has dozens of channels.) Multiple channels avoid interference between stations and allow switching among channels to achieve reliable communications.

You will have to consider the band used in your area before you choose equipment. Unless you purchase a receiver with coverage on both low- and high-vhf bands, you must identify the desired band you wish to monitor. Fortunately, it is usually a simple matter to look at the antenna on a mobile unit and determine its band of operation. There is an occasional exception to the rule, but in virtually all instances, antenna length varies with band and frequency Antennas are generally based on a quarter of the radio wavelength.

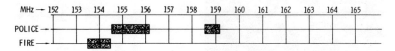

Fig. 2-3. Police and fire frequency assignments on high-band vhf.

Fig. 2-4. Mobile antenna used for low-band
vhf communications.

If you see a whip antenna on a police or fire vehicle that is approximately five to seven feet long, it is operating in the low band; that is, 30 to 50 MHz. The whip is generally mounted on the rear deck of an automobile or, in the case of an unmarked police car, on the front cowl in the style of a conventional auto-radio antenna. Since low-band whips are subject to impact on tree branches and other obstructions, they often have a spring-type mounting base, as shown in Fig. 2-4, to take up the shock. The base-station antennas for these services will also have a vertical element which is usually 5 to 7 feet long. Fixed antennas often have additional elements which droop outward from the base. These will be discussed later. Fig. 2-5 shows a typical low-band mobile antenna on a police car.

The high-band antenna is easy to spot because it is fairly short. A typical mobile antenna for the 150 to 174 MHz band measures approximately 18 inches long, as shown in Fig. 2-6. These antennas usually require no spring at the base (just an insulator) and are often mounted on a large flat surface such as a car roof or the center of a trunk deck. If

Fig. 2-5. Low-band antenna on police car.

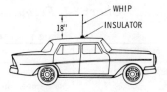

Fig. 2-6. Mobile antenna used for high-band vhf.

you see an antenna which is about 6 inches long on a vehicle, it is operating in the uhf band in the region of 450 to 470 MHz.

AVIATION BANDS

There is one major aviation segment of the vhf band, and it extends from 108 to about 136 MHz. About a third of the aviation band is of little use for monitoring. As shown in Fig. 2-7, the first 10 MHz is set aside for air navigation, with the remaining frequencies for communications. There is some voice communication on the navigation portion of the band, but you will probably not hear it unless you are located either next to an airport or near one of the hundreds of unmanned "omnirange" stations situated around the country. If you tune in a navigation station, you will probably hear whistles and growls in the speaker. These are either the instrument landing system signals used by aircraft or the electronic airways which guide aircraft on cross-country flights.

There is plenty of activity in the communications portion of the aircraft band. Above 118 MHz, it is often possible to hear pilots speaking from more than 100 miles away. You will also hear signals from planes in flight reporting to air traffic control stations on the ground. If you live near a small airport, you may pick up the advisory channel (unicom) for local aircraft. A detailed breakdown of how aircraft frequencies are assigned is given in Chart 2-1.

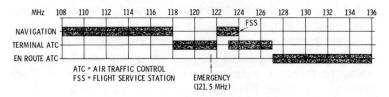

Fig. 2-7. Aviation assignments in vhf band.

Chart 2-1. Frequency Utilization Plan

AIR NAVIGATION AIDS

Frequencies	Use
108.1-111.9 MHz	ILS localizer with or without simultaneous radio-telephone channel operating on odd-tenth decimal frequencies (108.1, 108.3, etc.).
108.2-11.8 MHz	VOR's operating on even-tenth decimal frequenceis (108.2, 108.4, etc.).
112.0-117.9 MHz	Airway track guidance. (VOR's).

COMMUNICATIONS

Frequencies	Use
118.0-121.4 MHz	Air Traffic Control Communications.
121.5 MHz	Emergency (World-Wide).
121.6-121.9 MHz	Airport Utility (Ground Control).
121.95 MHz	Flight Test.
122.0 MHz	FSS's, Weather, Selected Locations, Private Aircraft and Air Carriers.
122.1 MHz	Private Aircraft to Flight Service Stations.
122.2, 122.3 MHz	FSS's, Private Aircraft, Selected Locations.
122.4, 122.5, 122.7 MHz	Private Aircraft to Towers.
122.6 MHz	FSS's, Private Aircraft.
122.8, 123.0, 122.85, 122.95 MHz	Aeronautical Advisory Stations (UNICOM).
122.9 MHz	Aeronautical Multicom Stations.
123.1 MHz	Search and Rescue (SAR) Scene of Action.
123.05 MHz	Aeronautical Advisory Stations (UNICOM) Heliports.
123.15-123.55 MHz	Flight Test.
123.15-123.55 MHz	Flying School.
123.6 MHz	FFS's, Airport Advisory Service.
123.6-128.8 MHz	Air Traffic Control Communications.
128.85-132.0 MHz	Aeronautical Enroute Stations (Air Carrier).
132.05-135.95 MHz	Air Traffic Control Communications.

SPECIFIC FREQUENCIES

Once you have identified the band you wish to hear, the next step is deciding on whether you will need a precise frequency within that band. Two-way radio services operate on specific channels and hold to these frequencies with great accuracy. Knowing exact frequencies is important if you are going to monitor with a *crystal-controlled* receiver. However, you will not have to know the exact frequency if the receiver is *continuously* tunable (like a regular table radio).

These differences are the subject of some detail in the next chapter, so we will consider only the way to determine the exact frequencies now.

If you have some association with the service—if you are a volunteer fireman or an auxiliary policeman for example, simply ask the appropriate authority. Channels of operation should be known at the base station. If this is not practical, you may consult listings compiled for the purpose. Such sources can usually be located by checking magazines which devote space to monitoring or shortwave listening. There are also directories which group allocated frequencies according to one or more states or regions.

3

Getting Started

If you have decided to take the plunge and monitor the bands, what is the next step? Searching through electronic catalogs, sending for maufacturer's literature, and browsing at local radio or electronic stores are all good possibilities. You will uncover a wealth of information about equipment, antennas, and accessories, but chances are you will raise as many questions as you will answer. Descriptive literature on receivers is filled with technical jargon which could confuse or mislead the prospective purchaser. So begin by taking stock of your needs; then evaluate the equipment and features available to meet them. There are many approaches to monitoring two-way radio, and the most expensive one is not necessarily the best one for your purposes.

Start by asking: Will the equipment be used for casual or for serious listening? The occasional listener might be content to tune a moderately priced portable or table model. A serious listener, like an auxiliary policeman or volunteer fireman, might want more costly equipment that contains circuits for sophisticated functions. A good place to begin is with the type of tuning.

CONTINUOUS TUNING OR CRYSTAL CONTROLLED

Assume that you have selected a band of interest. The next consideration is how you will tune the desired channels.

Receivers are designed with two basic tuning systems; the continuously tunable circuit and the crystal-controlled circuit. Not only do some sets combine the two, but there are also exotic circuits which automatically scan the channels. Each circuit has its benefits and its disadvantages.

Continuous Tuning

A continuously tunable receiver is almost always associated with the nonprofessional listener. It has a tuning dial which operates like that of a conventional a-m table radio. A pointer moves smoothly from the low to high end of the band, as shown in Fig. 3-1. An important advantage of the tunable dial is that it can tune every possible frequency within its band of operation. Another advantage is the lower cost. It is the least expensive method for providing complete frequency coverage.

Two disadvantages of continuous tuning are inaccurate frequency calibration and drift. Assume that you wish to tune a particular service assigned to a frequency of 153.77 MHz. Examine the dial of the tunable receiver and you may discover that it does not even indicate 153, but is marked every three or four MHz, e.g. 150, 154, etc. You can estimate the position of the desired channel on the dial, but the chances of landing on exactly 153.77 MHz are extremely remote. Therefore, it must be accepted that a continuously tuned receiver affords only approximate settings.

Next, assume that the tunable dial is adjusted to the desired frequency. You leave it there after turning off the receiver and expect to hear the same channel in the same dial position the next day. Now, *frequency drift* becomes

Fig. 3-1. Continuously tunable receiver.

apparent. The receiver circuits are subject to heat, humidity, and voltage variations which tend to disturb the long-term accuracy of the dial.

However, poor frequency calibration and drift are not reasons to reject the continuously tunable receiver. Considering its frequency flexibility and low cost, the tunable receiver is still a good choice for the casual listener.

Crystal-Controlled Tuning

Drift and inaccurate frequency selection would hardly be acceptable in an actual police, fire, or aircraft radio. Selecting a frequency must be done almost instantaneously, with no error. The universal technique for doing this is through crystal-controlled tuning. Instead of a smoothly tuned dial, the operator uses a switch that clicks precisely into position (Fig. 3-2). The switch activates a crystal within the receiver which tunes it with an accuracy of a few thousandths of one percent. Using this system, the radio operator can rapidly select a channel without even looking at a dial.

There are certain disadvantages to crystal control. For one, it usually limits the receiver to a few channels. Also, to keep the circuits tuned within proper range, crystals in a monitoring receiver are often restricted to a small segment of a band. The crystals are costly, too. Three or four of these quartz "rocks" can cost more than the total price of some tunable receivers. Despite these factors, a crystal-controlled receiver is often a good choice for the listener with more than a passing interest in tuning specific frequencies. Some circuits, like the one shown in Fig. 3-3, combines both crystal-controlled and continuous tuning.

Fig. 3-2. Four-channel crystal-controlled receiver.

Courtesy Petersen Radio Co., Inc.

Fig. 3-3. Receiver with both continuous and crystal-controlled tuning

SQUELCH CONTROL

In a conventional broadcast receiver, background noise, static crashes, and atmospheric hiss are quieted when a reasonably strong station is tuned in. In a communications system, however, signals are not continuous, but intermittent. This permits bursts of static between messages, which can be a considerable annoyance to the listener. The *squelch* circuit is used in professional communications equipment to spare the operator from noise during long monitoring periods when there is no signal. The squelch circuit senses when there is no signal, and mutes the speaker. It is like automatically turning the volume control all the way down. An incoming signal automatically restores the receiver to normal operation.

The nonprofessional receiver is also available with a squelch control. Whether you need it is a matter of listening preference. For the "dial twiddler," the squelch control will probably prove unnecessary. But when a receiver is turned on for long periods of monitoring, and the listener wishes to engage in some other activity, a squelch provides welcome silence. You simply adjust the squelch control (Fig. 3-4) until the background noise just disappears. It is important to adjust it while no signal is being received. The correct setting occurs when the noise just disappears, and a weak signal can restore normal operation of the receiver. A squelch control which is set too high reduces the sensitivity of the receiver and may cause missed signals.

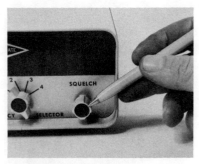

Fig. 3-4. Squelch control.

The squelch circuit on many low-cost receivers is apt to prove disappointing. Unless the designer has sufficient circuitry to work with, a simple squelch circuit may open only during reception of very strong local signals. The better squelch circuits are identified as "noise operated." This system has high sensitivity to weak signals and is reliable in operation. The action of a squelch circuit can often be judged by listening for a brisk, snap-action as the audio is restored, as if it were controlled by a switch. You may hear slight bursts of noise as stations stop transmitting, but the action is momentary and normal, even in costly circuits.

MANUFACTURER'S SPECIFICATIONS

Most manufacturers publish technical details to describe the performance of a receiver. Some specifications are valuable because they reveal what the receiver contains in the way of circuitry. Other items relate to how well a circuit may be expected to perform. To use specifications in comparing one receiver with another, however, may prove futile. The particular manufacturers may be measuring against different standards. Nevertheless, it might be informative to examine some specifications and note their approximate effect on receiver operation.

Frequency Range

Also called "tuning range," this term describes the bands of operation. If you purchase a low-band set, for example, expect to see something like "30-50 MHz" as the frequency-range specification. ("MHz" is an abbreviation for "Megahertz," a term which is identical to "Mc" or "Megacycles" used on older equipment.) Manufacturers may quote slightly different frequencies for coverage in the same band. Some receivers state "150-175 MHz" as the frequency range for the high band, while others give it as "148-174 MHz." These small differences may be ignored. Be certain that you understand the complete frequency coverage of a receiver before you purchase it. A set may say "Police" but not cover the correct band in your area.

Sensitivity

This specification is usually rated in microvolts, indicated by the symbol μV. A receiver requires a certain number of microvolts of signal from the antenna to achieve a given amount of quieting (decrease in background noise) in the loudspeaker. The more sensitive the receiver, the fewer number of microvolts are needed to achieve a given degree of quieting, rated in decibels (dB). If a receiver has a rated sensitivity of "2 microvolts for 20 dB quieting," the circuit would be improved by lowering the number of microvolts required for 20 dB of quieting.

The most sensitive receivers do a better job of pulling a weak signal from the background noise level. In selecting a receiver, however, it is usually wise to discount small differences in the sensitivity rating since there will be little perceptible difference to the ear. A receiver with mediocre sensitivity can often be greatly improved by improving the antenna system. Even the finest receiver may operate poorly on a small whip antenna near ground level or inside a metal structure.

Selectivity

This is a highly desired quality in communications. Selectivity refers to the ability of a circuit to reject signals which lie above and below the desired frequency. The higher the selectivity of a receiver, the more it slices away interference. The cost of a receiver is generally related to the quality of its selectivity. But it is also possible to have too much of a good thing. There is another aspect to selectivity that is worth considering.

If you are a casual listener who scans the band in search of activity, a receiver with poor selectivity can actually be desirable. The reason is that you can pick up more than one station simultaneously, and thereby expand your listening opportunities. If the stations are close together, you may hear two sides of a conversation being transmitted on different channels. Listening to the aircraft band on a low-cost portable is often more enjoyable because the selectivity is poor. While tuned to channels reserved for small aircraft, it is not unusual to hear a distant airline pilot without touching the dial.

The selectivity rating is generally given in decibels (dB) for a frequency span given in kilohertz (kHz). An example: Selectivity . . . 6 dB ± 12 kHz. Such a rating means that an interfering signal located 12 kHz higher or lower than the desired signal would be reduced by 6 decibels. The receiver would have poorer selectivity if the 12-kHz figure were 25 kHz. Usually, the manufacturer states selectivity at two points: at 6 dB and at 50 or 60 dB. Again, the lower the frequency span in kilohertz (kHz), the sharper the receiver selectivity.

Another item in the specifications which significantly affects selectivity is "dual conversion." It is a circuit which narrows the receiver response down for closely spaced or "adjacent" channels. In the conventional, or single-conversion circuit, the incoming channel is converted to a lower or intermediate frequency, where circuits can operate with greater selectivity. A popular intermediate frequency (i-f) in monitoring receivers is 10.7 MHz. A second i-f frequency is used in the dual-conversion receiver, usually at 455 kHz. The lower i-f frequency imparts a high degree of selectivity to the receiver. So, why not use 455 kHz in the single-conversion circuit? This would aggravate a second type of interference known as an "image." It takes a dual-conversion circuit to cope with both interfering stations and images. However, you may not require such high quality for most monitoring.

Modulation Acceptance.

This is another quality which is affected by receiver selectivity. Most low- and high-band signals are transmitted as fm (frequency modulation). Until a few years ago, fm signals conformed to an old standard which permitted a deviation of ± 15 kHz. As the bands grew crowded, the FCC changed the deviation standard to ± 5 kHz, or "narrow band," which permits more channels to occupy a given portion of the band. Although the receiver you might purchase should receive both wide- and narrow-band fm signals, the more selective circuit will do a better job on the narrow-band signals. Almost all fm communication signals are now narrow band.

Squelch Sensitivity

In receivers equipped with a squelch control, this rating may be stated in microvolts. The advantage of a more sensitive squelch is that it will open the speaker on weaker signals. The result is fewer missed calls. A squelch rated at .18 microvolts, for example, would be more sensitive than one rated at 2 microvolts.

SELECTING A RECEIVER

Choosing the receiver to suit your needs is no easy task. There are at least a half-dozen possible approaches to the technical task of taking radio signals from the atmosphere and delivering them to the speaker with maximum intelligibility. There are simple systems for the casual listener and advanced circuits for the serious monitor. There is also the battle of the pocketbook to consider, since receivers with superior performance or versatility usually carry a higher price tag. Your listening situation may vary—from home, to car, or to a hand-carried portable—which also affects the choice of a receiver. An experimenter or hobbyist might choose the build-it-yourself route, and choose from kits and modules that may be fabricated into complete receiving systems. Next, we will consider these varied possibilities in some detail.

4

Converters

If you own an outomobile, there is more than an 80 percent chance that it has an a-m radio. Therefore, it is not surprising that engineers have developed a system which utilizes the a-m radio as part of a mobile receiving system. The instrument that makes this possible is the *converter*. It is a popular and practical unit for using an a-m radio as a monitor on higher frequencies. A typical converter is shown in Fig. 4-1. The idea has been used for decades by amateur operators to receive the higher-frequency ham bands. The standard amateur receiver usually ends near 30 MHz, and the addition of a converter raises its range to the 6-meter (50 MHz) and the 2-meter (144 MHz) bands. Used with a car radio, a converter can take 150 MHz, for example, and reduce it one hundred times to 1.5 MHz, which falls within the standard a-m broadcast band. The converter is small, easy to install, and convenient to operate. But before considering it further, you should be aware of certain limitations. You will also want to pick one that matches your monitoring needs.

HOW IT WORKS

As the name implies, the converter converts one frequency—the one you wish to monitor—into another frequency, which can be received by the regular a-m radio. The

Courtesy Tompkins Radio Products

Fig. 4-1. Typical converter plays through car radio.

converter electronically reduces the received signal to a signal within the standard broadcast band. The concept is shown in Fig. 4-2, as it might work for an aircraft con-

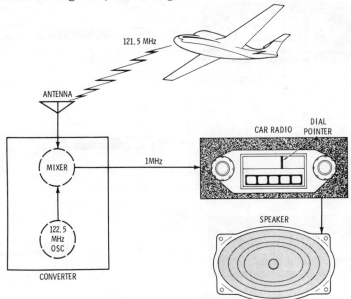

Fig. 4-2. How the converter operates.

verter in an automobile. The airplane is transmitting a signal on 121.5 MHz, a distress frequency. This is picked up by the regular car-radio antenna and applied to the mixer stage of the converter. Also feeding the mixer is a second signal, 122.5 MHz, from the oscillator stage. The two signals are combined in the mixer and a third signal, the difference frequency (1 MHz), appears at the output. This is a signal the car radio can handle, since 1 MHz falls nearly in the center of the a-m broadcast band. Thus, the aircraft signal is processed through the car radio in conventional fashion.

INSTALLING THE CONVERTER

Mounting a converter in an automobile usually requires little more than fastening its case to the underside of the dashboard (where you may find a hole already drilled). Once the unit is mounted in place, simply follow the three-step procedure shown in Fig. 4-3 to connect the antenna. First, the regular car antenna is unplugged from the a-m radio. The easiest way to locate the plug is to first find the coaxial

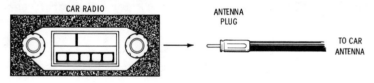

(A) Remove antenna plug from car radio.

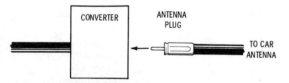

(B) Insert antenna plug into converter.

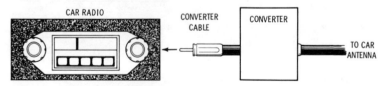

(C) Insert converter cable into car radio.

Fig. 4-3. Installing the converter.

antenna cable under the dash (the heavy black one) and follow it up to the radio with your hand. Grasp the shell of the plug, remove it, and then insert the plug into the back of the converter. There should be a standard plug and socket arrangement for a perfect match. Finally, the converter has a cable with the same plug as that used for the antenna cable. This is inserted into the open socket on the car radio.

That is all there is to installing the converter. Since the circuit draws very little current, the converter should work for long periods of time on its own small, internal battery (Fig. 4-4). This eliminates the need to tie into the electrical system of the car. If your converter depends on external power (Fig. 4-5), the manufacturer will probably suggest connecting it to the 12-volt source. This could be the accessory terminal on the back of the ignition switch or you could splice into the power lead which supplies the car radio. The converter should not need a ground wire because it is grounded by the antenna plugs and through the mounting hardware. Further details on converter installations are covered in Chapter 10.

After a converter is installed, you must "trim" the car radio. This is an adjustment to perfectly match the antenna to the radio. You have probably upset the match by adding

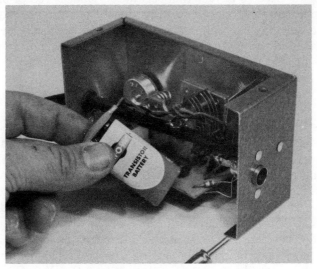

Fig. 4-4. Some converters operate on an internal battery.

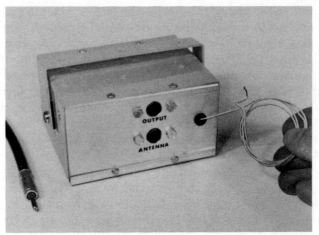

Fig. 4-5. Other converters use the electrical system of the car as a power source.

the converter in the antenna line. Correcting it is simply a matter of turning on the car radio and tuning to a weak a-m broadcast station near the upper end of the dial. The trimmer hole can be located in many car radios by placing your fingers on the antenna plug inserted into the radio. Within an inch or two of this location you will feel a hole that contains a small, recessed screwhead. A small screwdriver is used to adjust this screw for loudest reception on a weak station. Tune it carefully since it is a critical adjustment. In many car radios, the trimmer adjustment is located just behind the radio tuning knob, which is pulled off to gain access to the trimmer.

OPERATING THE CONVERTER

Let us say you are listening to the regular car radio and you wish to switch to monitoring. When you turn on the converter, several operations automatically occur. First, the car antenna is switched from the regular car radio to the converter. The converter output is connected to the antenna input of the radio. Power to the converter is turned on. Next, you turn the car radio dial to the frequency recommended by the converter maker, usually about 1500 kHz. This also may be done by setting up the frequency on the last radio pushbutton at the high end of the dial. While it offers fast frequency setup, this procedure will deprive you of one push button for a broadcast station. It is almost as simple to dial the pointer manually and listen for a characteristic "hiss" that tells when you have located the correct point. After these steps, tune the converter dial to select the desired frequency.

FIXED-FREQUENCY CONVERTERS

There are some major differences in converter design and operation. Consider the fixed-frequency converter, as shown in Fig. 4-6. This unit is designed to receive two channels. Since it is crystal controlled, you must know the exact frequency of the channels you wish to receive when the converter is ordered from the manufacturer or dealer. He will install the proper crystals in the oscillator stage to operate on a precise frequency.

The fixed-frequency converter can usually be ordered on almost any channel in a frequency range that begins at about 25 MHz and extends to more than 200 MHz. However, be sure to check the manufacturer's literature when more than one crystal is installed. There might be some restriction on how far apart the frequencies may be. It is not technically practical to produce a low-cost converter with one crystal on 32 MHz and another on 121 MHz, for example. To keep circuits simple, the channels usually must lie within a few megahertz of each other.

Sometimes you can tune more than one station with a single-channel fixed frequency converter. Recall that the car-radio dial is set to a point around 1500 kHz. But if you tune the car-radio dial while the converter is operating, you may hear other stations close to the fixed channel. This is

Fig. 4-6. Two-channel fixed-frequency converter.

Courtesy Tompkins Radio Products

because the car radio is acting as a "variable i-f"—a condition which enables it to tune a narrow portion of the converter band.

TUNABLE CONVERTERS

The second major converter type, the *tunable* variety, covers a wide frequency span without crystals (Fig. 4-7). Here the designer uses a variable capacitor which is manually tuned by the listener. (The car radio remains fixed at its recommended setting.) The advantage of a tunable converter is that it permits monitoring in almost any part of a band. However, you must select the band of operation when purchasing a converter.

Fig. 4-7. Tunable converter.

The disadvantage of the tunable converter is the lack of precision tuning. Unlike the crystal-controlled circuit, you could miss the desired signal by not being precisely tuned. It is also difficult to preset the dial with no signal on the air. This, of course, is no problem with the elaborate converters which combine both tunable and crystal-controlled operation, like the model shown in Fig. 4-8.

Fig. 4-8. Converter with both continuous tuning and crystal control.

A disadvantage in some converters is the lack of a squelch circuit. When signals are not received, you might have to endure ignition noise and static crashes in the speaker. Some manufacturers make converters with a built-in squelch circuit or offer it as an add-on accessory. If monitoring is to be done over long periods, the squelch control will reduce listening fatigue.

CONVERTER ANTENNA

Since the converter receives its signal from the same antenna that is used for the car radio, there may be some compromise in performance. This may not matter where signals are strong, but it could affect range in some areas, since each frequency or band segment requires a discrete antenna length for best performance. One trick for improving weak vhf signals from a car antenna is to adjust the length of the telescoping sections. While listening to a signal through the converter, attempt to vary the antenna for the least noise behind the signal. Your hand will probably detune the antenna and affect the result, so attempt to make a series of small changes, removing your hand from the antenna while listening for the result. Optimum reception on the high band (around 150 MHz) might require an antenna length of only about 20 inches.

CONVERTERS IN THE HOME

Some manufacturers state that their converters may be used with home radio or portables. They may supply a special loop which enables the converter to be placed next to an a-m radio with no further connection. The loop radiates the converter signal to the a-m radio antenna. The system works, but do not expect more than mediocre results. One problem is that you may not obtain good coupling between the converter and the radio. Sensitivity may be poor because many a-m receivers in the home are fine for the powerful, local broadcasts, but have inadequate gain for the weak vhf signals from the converter.

Another problem is that stations on a low-cost home radio may be grouped closely on the dial, leaving little space for the converter output signal. Finally, operation in the evening hours may be virtually impossible. The home radio will pick up dozens of distant broadcast stations and the result will be howling interference. This is less of a problem in the car radio because it is extremely well shielded by a metal case and accepts only the desired signals from the converter through a coaxial cable. There is no comparable protection in a home radio with a plastic or wood cabinet. Good vhf reception in the home usually calls for one of the other major monitoring methods described in the following chapters.

Fig. 4-9. Crystal-controlled converter for home and portable use.

Courtesy Electra Corp.

Fig. 4-9 shows a crystal-controlled home-type converter which works unusually well with a fair signal. This unit, primarily designed to work with transistor portable radios, will also operate with a table-type home radio. It is available either in single-frequency or two-frequency models.

AM OR FM

Although a radio receiver may be designed for a-m or fm reception, this does not apply to the converter. The converter circuit ignores the type of modulation (frequency or amplitude) and delivers the signal to the broadcast receiver. When the converter is operating on the low or high bands, the signal will usually be fm, while signals from aircraft will be a-m, or amplitude modulation. However, there is an a-m or fm consideration in the car receiver.

A regular car radio is an a-m receiver. Its detector circuit responds only to those changes in a radio carrier which represent amplitude modulation. What happens when an fm signal from the converter reaches the receiver? Fortunately, it is possible to hear acceptable fm on an a-m car radio. Although the radio has neither ratio detector nor discriminator (the standard fm detector circuits), the receiver will recover audio by "slope detection." In this process, the fm signal enters the i-f stages of the receiver and shifts frequency according to the audio information. These frequency changes cause the signal to slide in and out of the tuned i-f circuits. These variations produce ample voltage changes to convert fm to a-m.

One minor problem occurs when the fm signal is perfectly tuned to the car receiver. It may sound mushy and distorted. This is because the signal remains completely inside the boundary of the tuned i-f circuits. This condition can be quickly cured by tuning the dial slightly off to one side, which places the signal on the "slope" where it can be detected. Tuning the car radio will show where clearest audio is obtained.

5

Receivers

Police, fire, and aircraft receivers are packaged in many variations. Some models tune a solitary channel, others select one or more bands, and still others scan several channels automatically. There are sets which are built primarily for entertaining or short-wave listening but add a vhf band or two for monitoring. Before seeing examples of each major receiver type, there are some general considerations.

RECEIVER LOCATION

When tube-type circuits prevailed, it was simple to classify a receiver as for home, car, or portable use. A mobile set would be dc powered (6 or 12 Vdc) to operate from the car battery. The portable functioned from batteries, while a set for the home would operate from house current (117 Vac).

These distinct categories have nearly disappeared as solid-state circuitry has become widely used. Transistors and microcircuits allow the designer great freedom as to power source, which accounts for much equipment being capable of three-way operation. Such equipment operates equally well in the home, car, or as a portable. The outward appearance of a receiver, therefore, is no absolute guide to where it may be used. Some models may be carried as a portable, then may be converted to mobile use through a 12-

volt dc power cord and a connection to the car antenna. The manufacturers' literature should be carefully checked to find a receiver to fit your particular needs.

THE SUPERREGENERATIVE RECEIVER

The equipment we will describe operates almost exclusively on the *superheterodyne* principle. This is the basic design followed by almost every manufacturer. However, a second type, the *superregenerative* receiver, occasionally appears in the marketplace. The attraction is an extremely low price, since few components are needed for its simple circuit. Moreover, the superregenerative receiver can perform with the sensitivity of the conventional superheterodyne. Therefore, is it worth considering?

The main disadvantages of the superregenerative receiver are that it is difficult to tune and the dial calibration is only approximate. Also, the circuit operates with increasingly poor selectivity as the signals grow stronger, so it is difficult to separate stations on the dial. For these reasons the limitations of a superregenerative receiver should be considered carefully. Merely bringing your hand near the receiver antenna is often enough to detune the signal. The superregenerative should not be ruled out completely, however. If the limitations are acceptable it might provide some casual listening if you are willing to tolerate fussy, imprecise tuning.

SINGLE BAND RECEIVER

Let us examine some practical examples of receiving equipment. Although there are no rigid categories, we can draw dividing lines by using one of the most important criteria in choosing a specific model. That is the band coverage. The small receiver shown in Fig. 5-1 is typical of a single-band portable which covers the high band from 146 to 175 MHz. Such sets are also offered with low-band coverage from 27 to 50 MHz. They operate on batteries and include a built-in telescoping antenna. Such receivers are among the lowest-cost equipment and require fairly careful tuning to hear a station clearly once it is located on the dial. This is because of limited "bandspread." Also, the dial

Fig. 5-1. Single-band portable vhf receiver.

Courtesy Allied Radio Corp.

calibration is only approximate on most portables of this type.

Another single-band set for home use is shown in Fig. 5-2. The model shown covers the low band while an equivalent set is produced for the high band. Again, tuning is continuous. A new feature is added, however, which should be a welcome addition during long periods of monitoring in the home. It is a squelch control to quiet noise and static that would otherwise be heard in the speaker when no signal is being received. An additional feature, not apparent on the front panel, is an automatic noise limiter. This circuit

Fig. 5-2. Single-band vhf monitor for home use.

Courtesy The Hallicrafters Co.

Fig. 5-3. Mobile receiver for high-band vhf also has crystal-controlled channel.

reduces pulse-type static from passing cars or rotating machinery.

The next receiver, in Fig. 5-3, is clearly a mobile unit that is made for mounting below the dashboard with a bracket (supplied by the manufacturer). As in the sets just described, it has a continuously tunable dial. However, something new has again been added. This set also has a crystal for fixed-frequency operation. A selector on the front panel lets you choose between a crystal-controlled channel and the tunable dial. This is handy if you have a special interest in a certain channel and need to tune it accurately. The tunable dial lets you also monitor other channels on the band.

In the model shown, the crystal is ordered from the source where the receiver is purchased. It is important to supply the frequency you wish to monitor, since crystals are cut to order by the crystal manufacturer. After the crystal has been obtained, it is quickly installed by removing the cover from the receiver. The crystal is then pushed into a socket, a feature which allows the frequency to be changed at a future time.

A similar single-band receiver shown in Fig. 5-4 also has a tunable dial with provision for one crystal. The mounting bracket at the top of the case is for mobile operation and the circuit operates on either 12 Vdc or normal house current. One added feature, the headphone jack at the bottom left

Fig. 5-4. Single-band receiver for home or car.

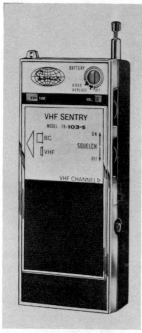

Courtesy Sonar Radio Corp.

Fig. 5-5. Portable crystal-controlled vhf receiver with standard broadcast band.

of the panel, might be desirable for someone who wants to monitor privately, or hear signals without disturbing other members of the family.

The portable receiver shown in Fig. 5-5 achieves some specialization of its own. For vhf monitoring, tuning is strictly crystal controlled for speed and accuracy. You can have two crystal-controlled frequencies in either the high or low band (depending on the model). The receiver can also

Fig. 5-6. Continuous tuning vhf receiver with standard broadcast band.

Courtesy Channel Master,
Div. of Avnet, Inc.

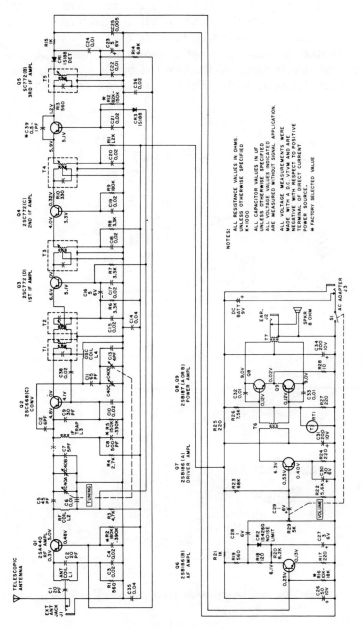

Courtesy The Hallicrafters Co.

Fig. 5-7. Circuit for a portable high-band vhf monitor receiver.

pick up the standard broadcast band to extend its utility beyond vhf monitoring. The circuit also features a squelch control for quiet operation between calls.

Another portable receiver is shown in Fig. 5-6. A model is available for each of the two vhf bands and both models are capable of receiving the a-m broadcast band. This con-

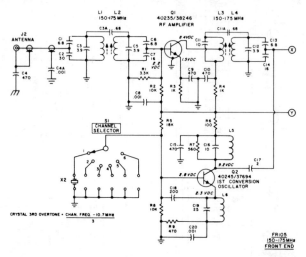

(A) High-band receiver.

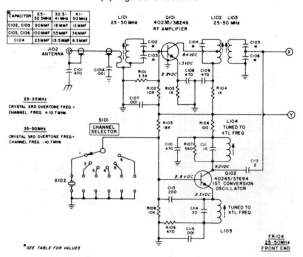

(B) Low-band receiver.

Courtesy Sonar Radio Corp.

Fig. 5-8. Front-end circuits for six-channel vhf receivers.

tinuous-tuning receiver also has a squelch control for quieter monitoring.

While a discussion of circuitry is outside the scope of this book, a schematic for a small portable vhf receiver is shown in Fig. 5-7. This is a single-band unit with continuous tuning on the high vhf band. It operates from a single 9-volt battery with provisions for an ac adaptor. The receiver circuit shown in Figs. 5-8 and 5-9 is a six-channel, crystal-controlled unit. It is available in both a high-band and a low-band model. The front-end circuits for both models are shown in Fig. 5-8. The circuit for the rest of the receiver is shown in Fig. 5-9. This unit features a squelch control and may be powered by 117-volt ac house current or 12-volts dc for mobile use. This is a dual-conversion receiver and employs two different i-f frequencies.

TWO-BAND RECEIVERS

A two-band model is illustrated in Fig. 5-10. It is a home-type set with individual dial calibrations covering both the low- and high-band services. A squelch control is also included. A further development of the two-band approach is the model seen in Fig. 5-11. Not only can you continuously tune the high or low bands, but you also have crystal-controlled tuning for both bands. The circuit makes provision for one crystal for each band, selectable from the front panel. Crystals are installed in sockets which are accessible after removing the top panel of the receiver (see Fig. 5-12).

The antenna terminals on a two-band receiver might have some special provision, as shown in Fig. 5-13. Note that two sets of input terminals are provided. They accept separate antennas, each designed for maximum efficiency in its own band, to obtain best receiving sensitivity. In the simpler receiver, one antenna might be used as a compromise for both bands.

MULTIBAND RECEIVER

Another receiver category is called "multiband." It includes receivers, like the one shown in Fig. 5-14, whose frequency coverage is vast. Such receivers usually represent an upward extension of the conventional short-wave band, which covers international broadcasting and other services in the high-frequency (hf) region from 3 to 30 MHz. Three vhf bands have been added to make this particular model cover low, high, and aircraft bands. In this case, the two top bands are marked "PS," meaning "Public Safety." They are actually the high and low vhf bands. The band shown as "vhf" is actually the aircraft band.

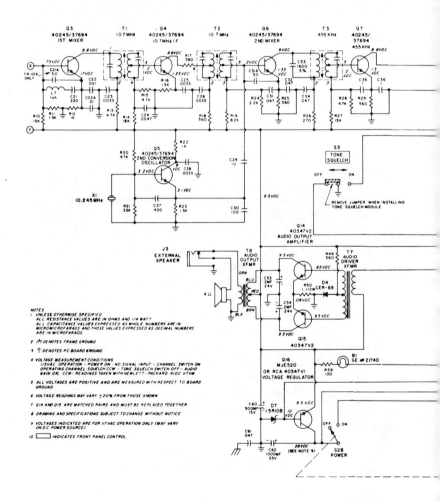

Fig. 5-9. I-f, audio, and power-supply

Receivers with such a broad frequency capability offer a huge number of listening possibilities from standard broadcast (a-m or fm) to shortwave and vhf. One potential handicap, however, is that they usually do not make any provision for crystal control on specific channels. This may be cumbersome when you must have precision while monitoring specific channels. But for the occasional listener, with wide interests, this type of receiver is ideal.

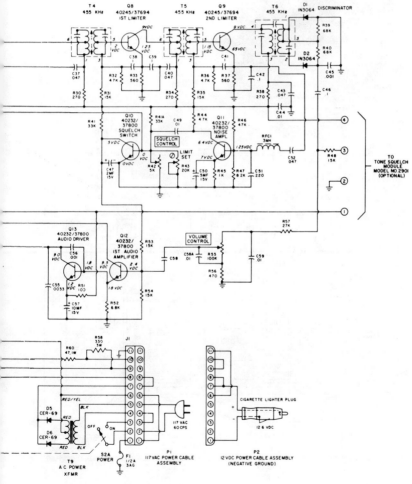

Courtesy Sonar Radio Corp.

circuits for high-band or low-band receiver.

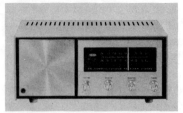

Fig. 5-10. Two-band vhf receiver for home use.

Courtesy Allied Radio Corp.

Fig. 5-11. Two-band vhf receiver with both crystal-controlled and continuous tuning.

Courtesy Lafayette Radio Electronics Corp.

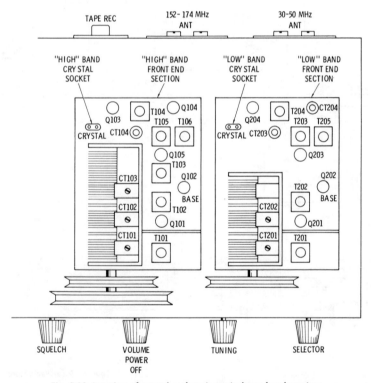

Fig. 5-12. Location of crystal sockets in typical two-band receiver.

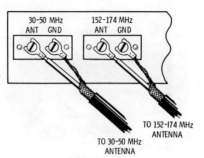

Fig. 5-13. Two sets of antenna terminals used on a two-band receiver.

WIDEBAND CRYSTAL-CONTROLLED RECEIVER

A receiver like the one shown in Fig. 5-15 occupies a special category marked by extremely wide frequency coverage, but on relatively few channels. It is possible to select any four frequencies within the considerable span from 2 to 200 MHz, and still have the advantages of crystal-controlled operation on several channels, but within one band. In most equipment, crystal frequencies must lie within a restricted frequency range.

In this circuit, however, the manufacturer utilizes an independent "front end," or tuning section, for each crystal frequency to permit tremendous frequency spacing. As the crystal selector is turned, plug-in cards containing the crystals and the tuned circuits are switched. The advantage is

Fig. 5-14. Multiband receiver includes three vhf bands, the shortwave band, and the standard broadcast band.

Courtesy Allied Radio Corp.

Fig. 5-15. Wideband crystal-controlled monitor.

Courtesy Petersen Radio Co., Inc.

that it becomes practical to monitor channels in each of the three major vhf bands (low, high, and aircraft). If desired, up to four channels within one band may be monitored. It is also possible to choose a crystal frequency outside the vhf bands for a service below 30 MHz.

SCANNING RECEIVERS

One novel approach to monitoring is achieved by frequency "scanning." This technique answers the problem of listening to several channels simultaneously. The receiver automatically scans up to eight different channels in the

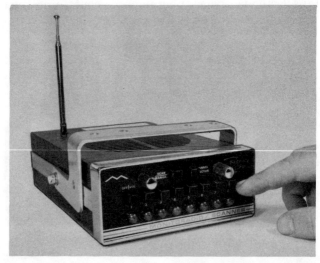

Courtesy Regency Electronics, Inc.

Fig. 5-16. Automatic scanning receiver.

Fig. 5-17. Automatic scanning receiver available for both vhf bands and uhf.

Courtesy Electra Corp.

band in an electronic operation equivalent to rotating the channel selector switch. Further, the receiver automatically stops on an active channel to permit monitoring. The example shown in Fig. 5-16 reveals eight pushbuttons, with a lamp below each button. When the receiver is turned on, the lamps flash from left to right as each channel is monitored. If there are no incoming signals on any channel, the flashing sequence automatically resumes to indicate the scanning action. The scanning rate is approximately 15 channels per second.

It is also possible to program the scanning receiver shown in Fig. 5-16. By depressing the desired channel buttons, the remaining channels are deactivated and the scanning action skips over those undesired positions. One application for this is when one channel in the receiver is vhf weather (on 162.55 MHz). Since that signal is continuous, it would arrest the scanning action. Thus, the pushbutton for that channel can be depressed manually whenever weather reports are required.

The scanning receiver shown in Fig. 5-16 is available only for the high band, covering 148 to 174 MHz. Also, the manufacturer recommends that for best sensitivity, the selected channels should lie within a frequency span of 8 MHz. The receiver shown in Fig. 5-17 is available in three basic models. One model covers the low vhf band (30-50 MHz), another model covers the high vhf band (150-174 MHz), and the third model is for the uhf band (450-470 MHz). The recommended frequency spread is 7 or 10 MHz, depending on the model.

6

Kits and Modules

The kit and module category falls between the factory-made equipment and the "home-brewed" circuits built by skilled experimenters. They make construction at home convenient by supplying hard-to-get components and eliminating the search through catalogs and electronic stores to complete a parts list. In the kit approach, a manufacturer usually supplies parts which are assembled by following step-by-step instructions. The module concept is usually a circuit section which is prefabricated at the factory and offered as a building block for the complete receiver. The module contains the critical circuits which might prove difficult to assemble at home without costly test instruments and skilled techniques.

There are two appeals in the kit or module approach. One is the satisfaction of doing it yourself. The manufacturer usually assumes no technical background on the part of the builder and the instructions are detailed enough that the circuits often operate soon after the last solder joint has cooled. The other attraction is that it is often possible to construct a kit or module receiver at a considerable saving over the price of a factory-wired unit. Equipment for home construction, however, should be carefully selected since there is a wide variation in what is available under the kit and module category. Some of them require that you know how to read and understand a schematic diagram while others may contain such rudimentary circuits that they operate only when signals are extremely strong. The beginner should consider only those items offered by reputable kit manufacturers. Only the more sophisticated builder might exploit the bargain items which call for considerable electronic know-how. Let us consider several examples of the kit and module approach.

THE COMPLETE KIT

A kit like the model shown in Fig. 6-1 provides virtually everything except the batteries. It is supplied with an elaborate construction manual that enables nearly anyone who can read to meet with quick success. Using little more than a soldering iron and screwdriver, the circuit is assembled in approximately eight hours. No test equipment is needed since the alignment process is done by ear. You simply adjust a series of coils while listening for the loudest hiss in the speaker.

There are techniques used in a kit of this type to eliminate the tricky wiring encountered at vhf frequencies. One is the prefabricated "front end." As shown in Fig. 6-2, this is a preassembled component which is fastened to the main chassis. It contains the critical rf amplifier, mixer, and local-oscillator stages which require layout and alignment beyond the skill of the average kit builder. The builder merely attaches the external signal and supply leads to the preassembled circuit. Another technique which eases construction is the printed-circuit board assembly (Fig. 6-3). Most small

Fig. 6-1. The complete kit.

Courtesy Heath Co.

components are simply inserted into the holes in the board and soldered in place. This assures correct spacing between the parts, especially in the i-f amplifier which operates at a relatively high frequency (10.7 MHz).

In choosing a kit, evaluate it in terms of the major circuit features discussed in earlier chapters. Some kits may prove more costly than some factory-wired receivers. If this sounds contradictory (in terms of saving money), the reason is apparent in circuit features and design. A kit can contain more stages, better selectivity, and elaborate circuits like a noise-operated squelch.

Fig. 6-2. Prewired "front end" supplied with kit.

THE PRINTED-CIRCUIT BOARD ASSEMBLY

Some manufacturers offer an item which blurs the line between the kit and the module. It is a printed-circuit board assembly like the one shown in Fig. 6-4. To assemble a complete converter, the builder chooses three basic boards; rf amplifier, rf mixer, and oscillator. The boards are quickly completed as the builder inserts parts and solders them to the copper foil. Final circuit items, like the converter case, switches, and connectors are furnished by the builder.

When the builder orders printed boards like these he must instruct the manufacturer as to certain specifications. The

Fig. 6-3. Printed-circuit board used in kit construction.

boards shown here, for example, are offered in "Lo" and "Hi" versions. These terms do not refer to the regular low and high vhf bands, but to 3-20 MHz and 20-170 MHz ranges chosen by the manufacturer. (The "Hi" kit, there-

Fig. 6-4. Printed-circuit board modules.

fore, covers *both* the low and the high vhf bands.) Also, the crystal used in the oscillator section must be specified in terms of exact frequency.

While such kits are easy to assemble, they may require a degree of technical knowledge in order to specify the correct values, then combine the boards into a working system. Consult the manufacturer's catalog or literature for these details in advance of purchase.

Fig. 6-5. Winding a converter coil.

A similar approach to converters is shown in Fig. 6-5. Here, the manufacturer supplies most parts, but omits such items as the cabinet and crystal. The builder may be required to wind a coil or do some other fabricating on his own. In fact, the circuit board may be a perforated board (as in this example) in which the builder mounts the components and connects them together by their leads or short lengths of wire. A converter of this type might be extremely low in cost mainly because it contains the fewest number of components required to receive a signal. While this eliminates much of the wiring of a more elaborate converter, do not expect sensitive performance. These simple converters may operate satisfactorily only in strong signal areas.

Fig. 6-6. Aircraft converter module.

THE POTTED MODULE

Yet another approach to monitoring is the "icecube" or potted module. An example of one for aircraft reception is shown in Fig. 6-6. These units are sold at very low cost and convert signals down to the broadcast band for reception on a regular a-m radio. However, you should know about one serious limitation. When the low-cost module has no provision for a crystal, it uses a "self-excited oscillator" to

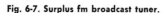

Fig. 6-7. Surplus fm broadcast tuner.

generate a required frequency in the a-m band. Unfortunately, oscillators of this type are very unstable unless they are properly shielded against hand capacitance. For this reason, these models are often difficult to tune and to keep on the desired frequency.

EXPERIMENTER MODULES

Bargains often appear on the market that the advanced experimenter can put to good use with some rewiring and conversion. Electronic skill, of course, is in order, since the builder must be able to understand a schematic diagram and have some knowledge of circuit operation. One such item, shown in Fig. 6-7, is actually the front end of a standard fm tuner. This particular unit was a manufacturer's "overrun" offered to the experimenter at a low price. In its original form, it receives 88 to 108 MHz (the fm broadcast band) and produces an intermediate-frequency (i-f) signal of 10.7 MHz. An enterprising experimenter could simply remove a turn or so from the coils, or spread the turns apart, to raise the frequency of the tuner to the aircraft band, for example, which begins at 108 MHz (directly at the top of the fm band). The output signal could then be fed into a conventional shortwave receiver tuned to 10.7 MHz. However, the builder should have sufficient circuit knowledge before attempting a conversion of this order.

7

Home Antennas

The antenna presents a great number of possibilities for improving a monitoring system. A simple whip can be adjusted to favor a particular frequency or you can erect a sensitive, high-gain antenna to extend your listening range beyond the local community. There are dual-band models which pick up two bands simultaneously or special antennas which are cut to an exact frequency of reception. But before looking at the practical matters, let us consider some of the properties of the vhf (and uhf) signal.

SIGNAL PATHS

The most important characteristic of vhf signals is that they travel a "line-of-sight" path. This differs from signals operating on the broadcast band, which hug the earth and travel around the curve on a "ground-wave" path. They also differ from short-wave signals which travel across oceans and continents by bouncing ("skipping") from the ionosphere. The vhf signal is a "direct wave" since it leaves the transmitting point and follows the most direct path to the receiving antenna.

The line-of-sight characteristic of a vhf signal makes it susceptible to the curvature of the earth. It is possible, when the transmitter and the receiver are sufficiently far apart, for the surface of the earth to protrude into the signal path and block reception. Increasing your antenna height is the general rule to follow if you wish to extend your receiving range. This principle is shown in Fig. 7-1. Assume that you wish to hear both a base station and a mobile unit located, say, more than about 40 miles away. Note that the mobile unit is close to the ground and emits a signal which extends to the horizon, then into space. Your receiver antenna fails to pick it up. The base station, however, is heard since there is sufficient height for the antennas to be in line with each other. A practical solution to this problem is to raise the receiver antenna so it can intercept the mobile signal. Height not only enables signals to clear the horizon, but intervening obstructions as well. Hills and tall buildings between you and the transmitting station can reduce or completely block reception.

These characteristics are not absolutely rigid or predictable. There is a certain degree of signal bending, or diffraction, over the tops of hills and around buildings. This could allow the signal to go into a "shadow" area. Further, signal absorption varies with changes of season. When summer foliage appears, it tends to attenuate signals, especially for frequencies at the higher end of the vhf band and on most of the uhf band. These effects may not be noticed on local signals, but could prove troublesome if long-range reception is planned.

Signals are also susceptible to "flutter." This is a rapid change in volume, usually caused as the signal bounces from some moving surface between you and the transmitter. It causes reflections which produce out-of-step signals and a corresponding shift in signal strength. When flutter is occasional and shifts in tempo, it is probably caused by a passing train or airplane. Continuous flutter that subsides during

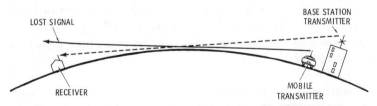

Fig. 7-1. Signal from base to receiver clears horizon, while mobile signal fails to reach receiver.

the late evening hours might be caused by reflections from near-by road traffic. An increasing flutter, heard while receiving a mobile signal, suggests that the vehicle is moving beyond your receiving range. In all of these cases, flutter can usually be reduced by improving your antenna system to boost overall signal strength.

TELESCOPING WHIPS

The whip antenna attached to many portable receivers works well if you wish to monitor local signals. Yet it is possible to improve its performance with almost no effort or expense. First, always "probe" for a good signal. If you walk around the room while listening, especially on the high band, you may hear great differences in signal quality. It is often possible to completely lose a signal by moving the radio only a few inches over a tabletop. The signal may be blocked my metal concealed in the wall or the ceiling.

Another phenomenon is cancellation. As the signal enters the room, it can bounce from a metal surface and return in the direction from which it arrived. There are now two signals, and they may be out of phase with each other. The results are signal cancellation and "dead" spots for reception in certain areas of the room. The same effect is occasionally caused by a person merely walking into the room. Thus, it is worth the effort to check the room for the best reception location while listening with an indoor whip.

There is another technique for improving reception with a telescoping whip. Virtually all of these antennas have a collapsing feature to make the receiver convenient to carry. It also makes the whip an excellent tuning circuit, although the manufacturer probably never intended it for that function. Nevertheless, this feature can improve reception. Adjusting a whip to the correct length often means the difference between hearing or losing a weak station.

As you may recall, the length of an antenna generally depends on its operating frequency. The low-band antenna is about 6 feet long, while a high-band antenna is around 18 inches long. The aircraft antenna is about 2 feet long. The different lengths are the result of tuning the antenna to a particular frequency. These factors can also apply to the whip antenna on a portable receiver. The manufacturer selects a whip length according to several compromises. First, the set may tune the complete vhf band, which means that a fully extended antenna may tune only one frequency with optimum efficiency. If you tune other stations on the band, receiver sensitivity may vary. Also, the receiver might be a two- or three-band model. When the whip is fully extended, it might be most effective on the lower bands, and suffer on high-band reception.

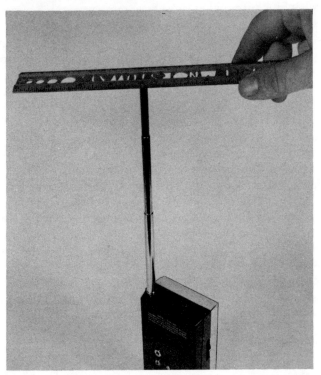

Fig. 7-2. Adjusting a telescoping whip antenna with a nonmetallic object.

A cure for this problem is often possible, by adjusting the length of the whip for best reception. This procedure may produce surprising results on weak signals. To find the best whip length, start by carefully tuning the station. This is most easily done by listening for a drop in background hiss, rather than louder voices in the speaker. Next, lower the antenna from its fully extended position in steps of about

Fig. 7-3. S-meter located at left end of tuning dial.

an inch at a time. This is almost impossible to do with your hand because body capacity will detune the antenna and make the results difficult to evaluate. Touch the tip of the antenna with a nonmetallic object. Press the antenna tip down, as shown in Fig. 7-2, while keeping hands and body well away from the antenna.

Judging the best whip position is easiest when the receiver has an S-meter, as shown in Fig. 7-3. The whip is adjusted until the maximum meter reading is obtained. (The needle may not move when the signal is extremely weak.) When the receiver has no indicator, try listening for the greatest drop in noise level.

Despite the small size and generally low mounting position, a whip often does a good job on local signals. If you wish to improve antenna sensitivity, you must move up to more elaborate antenna systems. Let us look at typical antennas that might serve this purpose.

Fig. 7-4. Ground-plane antenna.

Courtesy New Tronics Corp.

GROUND-PLANE ANTENNAS

A popular stationary receiving antenna is the *ground plane* (Fig. 7-4). Not only is it a good receiving antenna, but it is also commonly used at the transmitting end. A ground plane antenna is quickly recognized by a vertical radiator (or whip), with three or four radial elements protruding from its base. The radials, which often droop at an angle, give the antenna its name. They create the electrical ground plane required by the vertical whip. The advantage of this arrangement is that the ground plane may be located at any height above earth ground.

Fig. 7-5. Ground-plane antenna with adjustable elements.

Courtesy New Tronics Corp.

Another important quality of a ground antenna plane is that it is nondirectional (or *omnidirectional*). It picks up signals equally well from all directions. This is important in two-way radio since the position of mobile units is variable and unpredictable.

Manufacturers offer ground-plane antennas for both low- and high-band operation. If monitoring will be exclusively in the low-band region of 30 to 50 MHz, you can obtain a ground plane pretuned at the factory to approximately 40 MHz. This compromise setting works reasonably well over the whole band. Since the antenna is mounted outdoors at some height, performance should prove quite satisfactory through the band.

The ground plane offered for high-band operation may require some adjustment for best results, especially with weak signals. This is usually done in one of two ways. Some manufacturers offer ground planes with adjustable, or telescoping sections, as shown in Fig. 7-5. This provides a method for tuning the elements to a desired frequency or frequency grouping.

A second method is to provide a "cutting chart" and instruct the user to cut the vertical whip and radials to a size which tunes the antenna to the desired frequency. If the listener wishes to tune a whole band, he can cut the elements to a compromise length, as is usually done for the low-band antenna. An example of a cutting chart is shown in Fig. 7-6. You can see that one antenna can be cut for any

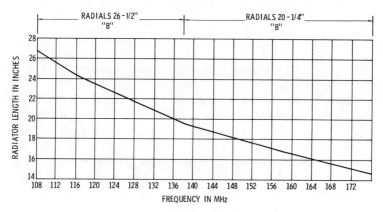

Fig. 7-6. Cutting chart for ground-plane antenna.

frequency from 108 to 172 MHz. Thus, it may cover the aircraft band as well as the high vhf band. The same antenna may be cut to the uhf band for any point between 400 and 470 MHz by using another cutting chart provided with the antenna. The actual antenna elements are shown in Fig. 7-7. After the vertical radiator and the radials have been cut to size, they are sealed by a plug at the top and ball tips at the radial ends.

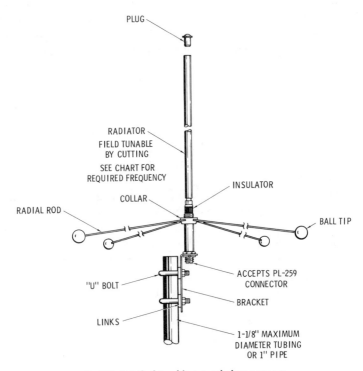

Fig. 7-7. Detail of tunable ground-plane antenna.

Assume that you are interested in tuning the complete high band, from about 152 to 174 MHz. Here you would choose the cutting dimensions for the midfrequency of approximately 163 MHz. If the aircraft band is the only one you will want, the center frequency is 123 MHz. If you wished to compromise over a wide range of 108 to 174 MHz, and therefore tune both the aviation and the high band, the center frequency would fall at about 140 MHz.

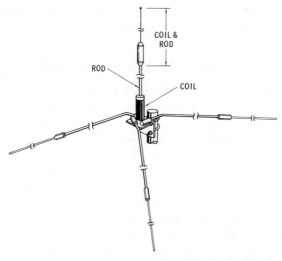

Fig. 7-8. Dual-band ground-plane antenna.

DUAL-BAND ANTENNAS

With the advent of dual-band monitoring receivers, which tune two bands, designers have come up with dual-band antennas to match them. These types maintain performance over a wide range by using coils which resonate on two bands simultaneously. An example of an antenna which can tune both the high and the low bands without readjustment is shown in Fig. 7-8. There are two coils, one at the base, and one near the center, which tune the antenna to the two bands.

Another adjustable-type antenna is shown in Fig. 7-9. It differs from the ground plane design in that no radials are

Fig. 7-9. Antenna adjustable from 135 to 180 MHz.

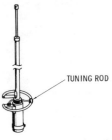

used. The manufacturer provides the dimensions for adjusting the elements to the desired frequency.

AIRCRAFT-RADIO RECEPTION

Little has been said about receiving signals from aircraft, for good reason. Unless you live within a steel building, reception from aircraft is usually excellent with only a telescoping whip or short length of wire attached to the antenna socket of the receiver. Signals should easily penetrate a roof made of wood or other nonmetallic materials. Signals from distances of 100 miles are common from cruising aircraft and such signals usually have an absolute range of 200 miles.

If you wish to monitor a control tower or other ground-based radio facility, the reception problem is severe. Line-of-sight transmission, coupled with the low power generally emitted by aviation ground stations, make monitoring difficult at more than about ten miles over land. However, these low-power stations have little difficulty in communicating with airborne equipment. When you wish to receive ground stations in the general area, you might have to erect an antenna specifically cut to the band and positioned as high as possible. Fortunately, the dimensions for an aircraft-radio antenna are quite small (about 2 feet), so mounting is simplified.

8

Mobile Antennas

An antenna for monitoring vhf signals while moving over the road can take several forms. If you want highest signal sensitivity, there are models designed especially for one frequency. For broader coverage, you might consider a two-band antenna. There are also models which share signals between your a-m radio and the monitor receivers.

A-M BROADCAST RECEIVERS

Connecting the monitor receiver to your regular car radio antenna is an attractive possibility, since it eliminates further antenna installation. In fact, if monitoring is done through a converter connected to the a-m radio, this is the standard arrangement. The manufacturer provides a switch for instant antenna changeover between the converter and the auto radio.

The length of an auto-radio antenna, about 4½ feet, places it somewhere between the low and the high vhf bands. Therefore, it is a compromise for signals in either band. The convenience of such an arrangement, however, may far outweigh the shortcomings of the antenna. It should operate reasonably well where great range is not expected and most monitoring is local.

To improve the performance of the regular auto-radio antenna, some manufacturers recommend that you adjust the elements to a height of about 18 inches for reception of high-band vhf signals. This may work, but it could also cause a deficiency in standard a-m reception. Another problem with using the regular antenna occurs when the monitor is a completely separate receiver. These sets do not routinely provide an antenna changeover switch like the ones built into converters. One answer for feeding the regular car whip into the separate monitor is to install a changeover switch under the dashboard. Details on how you can make such a switch are covered in the chapter on installation techniques.

MULTIBAND ANTENNAS

One solution for covering a number of bands is a multi-band antenna. A typical unit, shown in Fig. 8-1, covers both low- and high-band vhf, as well as standard a-m. Not only does it eliminate antenna switching, but it also replaces the existing a-m whip. Therefore, no additional holes are required in the car body. The antenna achieves its multiband performance by several modifications shown in the illustra-

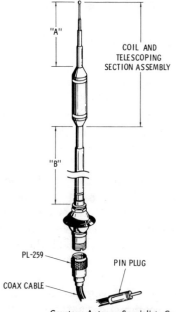

Fig. 8-1. Tri-band mobile antenna.

Courtesy Antenna Specialists Co.

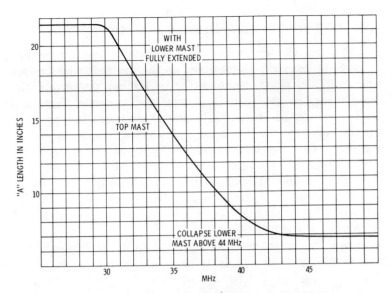

Fig. 8-2. Adjustment chart for low-band operation of tri-band antenna.

tions. There is a loading coil which electrically shortens the whip. A chart is supplied (Fig. 8-2) for adjusting the elements to optimum length. Reception on 35 MHz, for example, requires the top section "A" to be adjusted to 14 inches, while the lower mast "B" is fully extended. It is also possible to adjust the antenna to the center of a band for general monitoring.

An antenna of this type has an additional component. It is a coupler (Fig. 8-3), mounted under the dashboard and connected to the outside antenna whip and to any combination of receivers: a-m, low band, and high band. If one plug is not needed, a 47-ohm resistor is connected across it to preserve the electrical balance of the system.

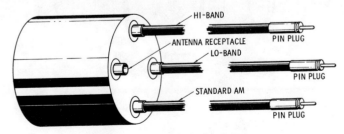

Fig. 8-3. Coupler used for tri-band antenna.

LOW-BAND AND HIGH-BAND ANTENNAS

The most efficient antennas for mobile monitoring are quarter-wavelength ships tuned to the desired band or frequency. They are the choice for maximum range and the least interference. To obtain good performance, these antennas should be located in a favorable mounting position on the car. For the low band, it means a whip of approximately 5- to 7-feet long, usually located on the trunk deck. Some whips are available with a ball-type mounting (Fig. 8-4) for side-mount installations. This type of mounting is often required on a truck which has no broad, horizontal surface other than the roof. (A low-band whip on the roof is too tall for practical use.)

When the quarter-wavelength whip is purchased, the manufacturer may supply it in a length that is tuned to the lower end of the band. For example, it could be 102-inches long for a frequency of approximately 27 MHz. When the antenna is to be used on higher frequencies, the instructions direct the installer to cut the whip to shorter length. Other models may be pre-cut to the center of the band (about 40 MHz) and require no further alteration.

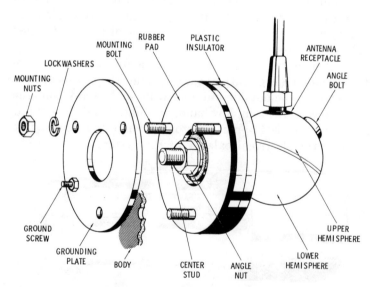

Fig. 8-4. Detail of ball-type mount for whip antenna.

Next, consider the high-band whip. The most effective position on the car is the center of the roof. It is an ideal location because the element is very small and needs the height advantage of the roof. Although this is practical for vehicles engaged in two-way communications, only the more serious monitoring listener would choose the roof-top location. It results in the best-performing antenna system but is one of the most difficult to install. It requires a hole to be drilled in the car roof and a cable fished through headliner and down a window post. (If you want to attempt the job, some details are given in the chapter on installation.) Another location for a high-band whip is on the trunk deck. This position may give some directionality to the pickup pattern, but it should prove satisfactory for reception in all but the most demanding installations. The front cowl or rear fender of the car are also possible mounting positions.

NO-HOLE MOUNTINGS

Some antenna manufacturers produce special antennas which require no holes to be drilled into the car. These models are generally classed as temporary antennas, but enjoy considerable popularity because of simplified installation. One type is the gutter mount model shown in Fig. 8-5. The manufacturer supplies a spring-loaded clamp which opens with a squeeze of the hand, then grips the U-shaped channel in the rain gutter on the car. The cable is then routed in through a window. In another type, the gutter clamp is fastened into position with screws. Some models have base springs to prevent damage if the antenna should strike an object.

There is also the magnetic mount. A powerful magnet in the base of the antenna adheres to a flat surface on the car (Fig. 8-6). The manufacturer states that the antenna will remain in position while the car is traveling at any legal speed. Again, the cable is routed through an opening, such as the window, for the simplest installation.

One popular antenna which requires no holes in the car body is the trunk-lid mount. It is a conventional antenna with a special mounting bracket (Fig. 8-7) that fits into

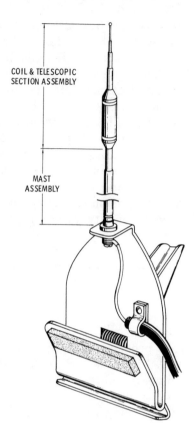

COIL & TELESCOPIC
SECTION ASSEMBLY

MAST
ASSEMBLY

Fig. 8-5. Gutter mount antenna.

Courtesy Antenna Specialists Co.

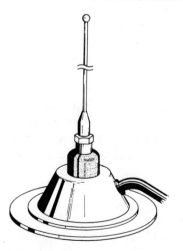

Fig. 8-6. Mobile antenna with magnetic
mounting base.

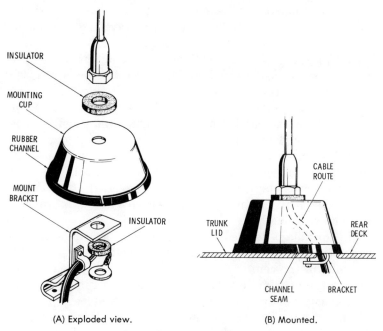

INSULATOR

MOUNTING CUP

RUBBER CHANNEL

MOUNT BRACKET

INSULATOR

CABLE ROUTE

TRUNK LID

REAR DECK

CHANNEL SEAM

BRACKET

(A) Exploded view.

(B) Mounted.

Fig. 8-7. Trunk-lid antenna mount.

the crack between the trunk lid and the car body. Set screws are used to tighten the clamp permanently into position. After installation, it is still possible to open and close the trunk lid in normal fashion. However, on certain autos (notably those of "fastback" shape), the whip may strike the rear window when the trunk is opened. This problem is cured by installing the whip off-center, or at the side of the lid.

CUTTING THE QUARTER-WAVELENGTH ANTENNA

The manufacturer either cuts an antenna to a given frequency or provides the user with a cutting chart. Sometimes, the buyer is expected to do his own calculating to determine the final antenna size. This is done by knowing the antenna type and applying a simple formula. It is based on the fact that the fundamental antenna type for 2-way communications is the quarter-wavelength vertical. There are variations, but when the antenna is a straight whip, with no coils, it usually operates as a quarter-wavelength element. This length is approximately 6-feet for the low band, and 1½ feet for the high band. Some low-band antennas have spring bases which resemble coils, but these are disregarded since their function is mechanical.

For most listeners, it is practical to cut the antenna for the middle of the band. Only when maximum sensitivity is required should an antenna be cut to an exact operating frequency. Such precision may be important for transmitting, but electrical conditions are less critical when an antenna serves only for receiving. However, if you want to figure the final length of a quarter-wavelength whip, use the following method:

The formula is derived from the physical length of a radio wave at a given frequency. Take the frequency 40 MHz, for example, in the center of the low vhf band. It has a wavelength of approximately 24 feet, as shown in Fig. 8-8A. The wave consists of two identical, but opposite, halves (positive and negative). To receive the wave, an antenna must be only one-half wavelength long. This is because half of the wave (the positive portion, for example) fills the antenna element with a signal during a given instant. Then, a reversal occurs and the other half of the signal enters the elements. Thus, it takes only a half-wavelength to intercept the complete signal. In this example, the antenna would need only be 12-feet long (Fig. 8-8B).

In a practical antenna, however, it is possible to eliminate *half* of a half-wavelength antenna. This is done by using a ground system to make up the missing half. This is shown in Fig. 8-8C, the quarter-wavelength antenna. The

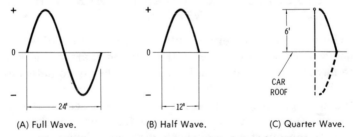

(A) Full Wave.　　　　(B) Half Wave.　　　　(C) Quarter Wave.

Fig. 8-8. How quarter-wavelength antenna is derived for 40 MHz.

car roof below the antenna electrically acts as the other quarter-wavelength. In this manner, the antenna is reduced to a convenient size for a mobile installation, approximately 6 feet. For the base-station antenna, the missing quarter-wavelength can be provided by the ground-plane action of radial elements drooping outward at the bottom.

If you want to calculate a quarter-wavelength antenna on any frequency, use the formula:

$$\text{Quarter Wavelength} = \frac{234}{\text{frequency}}$$

where,

The quarter wavelength is in feet,

234 is a constant which takes into account the speed of a radio wave and a correction factor because the speed of a radio wave in the feedline is slower than in space,

The frequency is in Megahertz.

For example, the quarter wavelength at 40 MHz is:

$$\text{Quarter wavelength} = \frac{234}{40}$$

$$= 5.85 \text{ ft.}$$

$$= 5' \, 10''$$

9

Home Installation

Setting up for monitoring at home may take only a few minutes or it may take as long as a day or more. You can extend a telescoping whip on a receiver or attach a short length of wire in moments to capture local signals. As described earlier, an indoor antenna should be varied for best reception and the receiver should be located in the most favorable part of the room. Now, we will consider further details for securing good reception with more elaborate antennas and techniques.

RECEIVER LOCATION

Avoid locating the receiver next to a heating source (radiator) or within a foot or two of a fluorescent lamp, which is a prolific generator of radio noise. (Other forms of interference and their cures are described later.) If monitoring is to be mostly on one channel, or if you have crystal-controlled reception, the receiver can be located beyond immediate reach. In these cases, there is no need for frequent retuning.

If your receiver can operate from either house current or internal batteries, do not overlook the benefit of battery operation at home. Listening with batteries is somewhat more costly than operating from the ac line, but this will greatly increase the versatility of the set. It is very convenient to have the option of carrying the receiver to any

Fig. 9-1. Coaxial cable used for ground-plane antenna.

room in the home or outdoors, thereby ignoring the need for an ac outlet.

If you are planning to use an outdoor antenna, receiver location becomes more important. The antenna cable is often brought in through a window frame and this might influence where the receiver is to be located. The antenna cable required for most outdoor antennas is a coaxial cable with an impedance of approximately 50 to 75 ohms. It is a round cable (Fig. 9-1) that does not easily run around baseboards and door frames, as in the case of flat TV twinlead. To avoid long runs, you might want to locate the receiver near the window the cable enters.

Coaxial cable has the advantage that it can be run almost anywhere without short circuiting the signal. It requires no standoffs or insulators and may even be run underground or along a metal surface, as shown in Fig. 9-2. With this

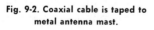

Fig. 9-2. Coaxial cable is taped to metal antenna mast.

installation flexibility, you can run the cable through the basement, a closet, or the attic to reach the receiver.

ATTIC ANTENNA

Do not overlook the possibility of an attic antenna installation. It affords the advantage of height and complete freedom from deterioration by weather. The cable can be routed out a window near the receiver, up the side of the house, and into the attic through a vent or similar opening. In this manner, a difficult wiring route through walls can be avoided.

The problem with some attic locations is that nearby metal may shield or distort the signal. Roofing material, if made of asphalt shingle or some other nonconducting material, will not significantly obstruct the signal. Conduit, plumbing pipe, rain gutters, and other metallic objects close to the antenna may reduce performance. They should be avoided by keeping the antenna spaced as far as possible from other electrical conductors. Allow for metal that might lie hidden just on the other side of an attic wall, such as, electrical and telephone cables, plumbing, or rain gutters. Despite these potential problems, an attic location may provide fine reception because it lifts the antenna clear of obstructions near ground level, while offering protection against the elements.

SHARING THE TV ANTENNA

It may occur to some listeners that the television antenna might also serve for the monitoring receiver. Television does, in fact, occupy large sections of the 30 to 300 MHz band. The low vhf band is located just below TV Channel 2, while aircraft and high bands lie between TV channels 6 and 7. Since the TV antenna might be in a high outdoor location, it might also be suitable for monitoring two-way radio signals.

TV antennas vary in their ability to tune two-way radio bands. Many models have "peaks" which favor only the TV channels and operate with poor sensitivity on other frequencies. Also, the TV antenna is always horizontal (in the

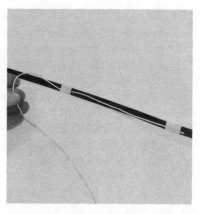

Fig. 9-3. Coupling to TV antenna lead-in.

USA) since the TV signal is transmitted with horizontal polarization. Virtually all two-way radio communication utilizes vertical polarization. TV antennas are also directional, whereas two-way radios usually operate with nondirectional patterns. Finally, a TV antenna lead-in is generally 300-ohm impedance, while coaxial cable, at 50-to-75-ohms impedance, is common to monitoring receivers.

Despite these obvious limitations, a TV antenna might provide good signals to a monitoring receiver. One trick used by some experimenters is to "steal" the signal directly from the antenna lead-in feeding the TV receiver. Run a length of insulated wire from the antenna terminal of the receiver to the TV antenna lead-in (Fig. 9-3). Temporarily tape about a foot of the insulated wire against the antenna lead-in. Experiment with the position and length of the insulated wire for best reception at the monitoring receiver. There is no direct electrical connection in this arrangement. There is merely a capacitive pickup between the monitoring receiver and the antenna lead-in. According to theory, the TV twin lead should not be emitting signals, but the practical line is not perfect. It may supply enough signal energy to operate the monitor receiver, and end your antenna installation. If you are of experimental bent, and are having some difficulty securing good signals, this unorthodox approach might solve the problem.

Another form of sharing is to mount the monitoring antenna on the mast being used for the TV antenna. Many vhf and uhf communication antennas are small and add negligible weight and wind loading to the array. The problem becomes one of spacing the antennas to prevent interaction between elements and possible loss of performance on certain TV channels. A recommended spacing from the TV antenna is approximately 8 feet. An antenna for the high vhf band, however, is so physically small that a position a few feet above the TV antenna might not disturb TV reception. A low-band antenna cut for about 30 MHz would prove too unwieldy to share the mast since it could increase the overall height by about 8 feet.

Fig. 9-4. Antenna mounted in a high location on its own mast.

ROOFTOP ANTENNA

An antenna designed for vhf or uhf mounted on its own mast, high and in the clear, affords the best possible reception (Fig. 9-4). A typical model has a U-bolt clamp at the bottom for simple connection to a mast as shown in Fig. 9-5. The hardware offered for TV installation is admirably suited to erecting monitor antennas. Mast sections are available in standard lengths of 5 and 10 feet, and mountings are widely available for fastening to a chimney, eaves, roof, pipe, wall, or masonry.

If there is any choice in mounting location, you should consider certain factors. A chimney mount is one of the easiest to install but may cause some deterioration because of soot and other deposits. If the antenna is mounted on the chimney, it should be checked after about one year of operation and the lower elements should be cleaned if they are blackened where radial rods meet the vertical whip (Fig.

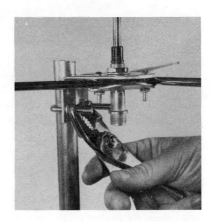

Fig. 9-5. Antenna mounted with U-bolt clamp.

9-6). This procedure reduces signal leakage between the active and the grounded elements of the antenna.

If you live near a busy highway, try to mount the antenna on the side of the house away from the traffic. Vehicles radiate considerable ignition noise, and a greater distance away from the source can reduce interference in the receiver. This

Fig. 9-6. Cleaning the antenna insulator.

type of noise usually will not affect strong local signals, but could make the weak ones difficult to hear. Ignition noise pickup may also affect the squelch system. You may set the squelch for silence during a no-signal condition, but the circuit trips open on ignition noise. If you adjust the squelch to prevent the noise, the squelch circuit may not trigger the receiver on weak signals. The result is missed calls.

ANTENNA SELECTOR SWITCHES

Multiband monitors that tune more than one service present a special antenna problem when you want to hear distant signals. If an antenna is chosen for high sensitivity in one band, it may produce poor results on other frequencies. One solution is a multiband antenna which simultaneously tunes to more than one band. Another possibility is a selector to switch between two antennas. One antenna could be an outdoor type, and the other could be a short indoor wire on another band. A suitable selector is a simple bakelite knife switch shown in Fig. 9-7. Placed near the receiver, it provides an instant choice between signal sources. Where an antenna cable is required, the coaxial cable may be 50

Fig. 9-7. Antenna selector switch.

ohms (RG-58/U) or 72 ohms (RG-59/U). To wire the switch, strip away the outer plastic jacket of the cable and expose both inner conductor and braided shield. Connect the inner conductor to the screw terminal and twist the strands of the shield together, as shown in Fig. 9-8. Note that the shields of the three cables will be connected together to form a common ground. Solder the shields together, then use tape to insulate them from possibly shorting against the switch terminals. If one of the antennas is a single-wire indoor antenna, it is connected to the switch instead of a coaxial cable, as shown in Fig. 9-8.

Another special situation occurs for monitoring receivers which operate on two bands with dual "front ends." These

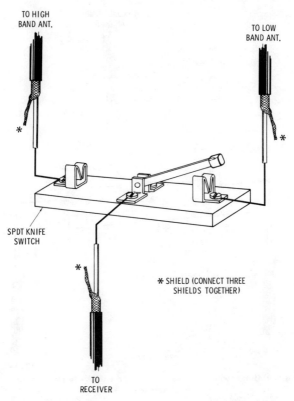

TO HIGH
BAND ANT.

TO LOW
BAND ANT.

*

*

SPDT KNIFE
SWITCH

*

* SHIELD (CONNECT THREE
SHIELDS TOGETHER)

TO
RECEIVER

Fig. 9-8. Wiring switch to connect two antennas to a single receiver.

models usually have two sets of antenna terminals for connecting both high- and low-band antennas. If you wish to use a dual-band antenna instead of separate antennas, you can install a selector switch to feed the antenna to either the high- or the low-band terminal. A suitable arrangement is shown in Fig. 9-9. Again a knife switch of the single-pole, double-throw type is used, and the cable shields are tied together to form a common ground.

CONNECTING A CONVERTER TO A HOME RADIO

Most converters are designed to work with car radios and to plug directly into them. To use a converter with a home a-m radio, you must provide some method of introducing the

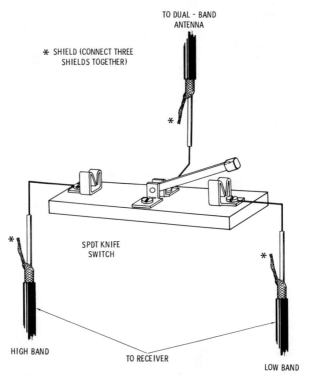

Fig. 9-9. Using switch to connect dual-band antenna to receiver with two sets of antenna terminals.

converter signal into the a-m receiver. A loop of wire from the converter to the receiver may prove satisfactory, but a more efficient technique is to make a coupling loop which tunes the converter output signal. Details of a home-made coupler recommended by one converter manufacturer are shown in Fig. 9-10. It is based on a converter output fre-

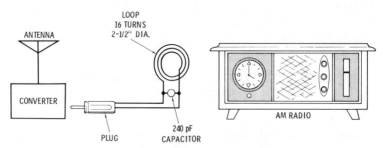

Fig. 9-10. Construction of loop coupler.

quency of 1500 kHz (the high end of the standard broadcast band). First, a loop is made from enameled wire (any size from No. 20 to No. 32) by winding the wire on a round shape with a diameter of 2½ inches. After winding 16 turns, remove the loop and tape it to keep the turns together. A 240-pF mica or ceramic capacitor is soldered across the two ends of the loop. Also connected to these points are the two lead wires which run from the loop to the converter. (Use ordinary insulated hookup wire.) If the converter has an output socket, connect a matching plug to the loop wires. Some converters already have an output cable and plug. In this case, connect the loop wires to the plug tip and outer shell.

To use the loop, tune the a-m radio to the desired frequency (1500 kHz, in this example) and move the loop around the radio cabinet to find the best position. Some experimentation will determine the most favorable coupling between the radio and the converter. If the converter has an output frequency much lower than 1500 kHz, you may have to reduce the tuning frequency of the loop if signals are poor. This can be done by adding turns to the loop or increasing the value of the 240-pF capacitor across the two loop leads.

10

Mobile Installation

Mounting receiving equipment in an automobile demands no great skill, but simple hand tools and careful planning are indispensable for this installation. There are some preliminary decisions, such as: where to locate the receiver, how to fasten it, and how to find a takeoff point for the electrical power. We will trace the major steps that apply to almost any type of monitoring instrument you might wish to install.

LOCATING THE RECEIVER

The most popular mounting location is under the lip of the dashboard, within arm reach of the driver. Possible mounting locations are determined by having someone temporarily hold the set in place while you sit in the driver's seat and reach for the controls. This procedure also reveals impractical locations. Press the accelerator pedal and check the other controls to see if the receiver interferes with their normal operation. It is easy to choose a handy location, only to discover later that you scrape your shins against the cabinet when you press the brake pedal.

Other factors affect a final mounting position. If the receiver has a tunable dial, it should be convenient to reach. A crystal-controlled receiver may be farther away, since the only tuning is done with a selector switch. You will not have to see numbers on a dial or tune with precision. The location, of course, ultimately depends on the car. Some autos have much open space under the dash, while others present slanting, obstructed areas. Many cars have ash trays just above a good receiver location. Be sure you can still remove the ash tray after the receiver is in place (Fig. 10-1). Do not overlook the possibility of mounting a unit to the left of the steering wheel. Just make sure that you do not block the parking brake or the headlight dimmer switch.

Some cars offer no spare room under the dash. This situation is usually overcome by "console" mounting, which is accomplished by locating the set on the floor (on the transmission "hump"). You can usually drill small holes in the floor and use some L-shaped brackets to mount the receiver. Sheet metal screws avoid the need for nuts, which might be difficult to install from underneath the car.

A hidden problem in dashboard mounting is the heating system of the car. It is possible to place the receiver in a blast of hot air and seriously upset transistors and other semiconductors. Heat causes frequency drifting, audio dis-

Fig. 10-1. Checking mounting location for converter under the dash.

Fig. 10-2. Check the air flow from the heater.

tortion, and sometimes "thermal runaway," which destroys transistors. It is advisable to determine the final receiver position while the heater air flow is fully turned on (Fig. 10-2). You may often avoid the blast areas by moving the receiver slightly to the left or right. If the car has adjustable vanes to direct the heater air flow, you might be willing to set them in one direction and leave them there.

Many receivers for mobile operation are supplied with mounting brackets (Fig. 10-3). If not, a suitable bracket may be fashioned from perforated strap used to suspend plumbing pipes. The bracket is bolted to the dashboard through holes in the underlip. Before drilling any holes, check the mounting area. You will usually find holes already punched by the manufacturer, and one or more of them might line up with your bracket. If you must drill holes,

Fig. 10-3. Mounting bracket and dc power cord for mobile operation.

check to be certain you are not drilling into a blind spot. You should be able to hold a nut above the drill hole to receive the mounting screw. Also, watch out for wiring harnesses that run inside the dashboard. Hold them away from the spinning bit as you drill. Before drilling, centerpunch a dimple into the dash metal. It could prevent the drill bit from skittering across the instrument panel.

CONNECTING TO THE POWER SOURCE

Some converters require no external power source because they operate from internal batteries. This is impractical in complete receivers because of the higher power drain. They must be connected to the electrical system of the car. Before making any wiring connections, consult the manufacturer's instruction manual. It may state special considerations for sets which operate from either house current or the car battery. In one model, the internal fuse protects the receiver only on ac house current. When the dc power cord is used for mobile operation, the internal fuse is automatically disconnected and a second fuse must be installed in the power line. These details will be found in the instruction manual.

The standard mobile power source is 12 volts dc, with the negative side connected to ground or to the car body. Most automobiles conform to this standard, but there are occasional exceptions. Some manufacturers allow for rapid conversion from positive to negative ground through a system of jumper wires on the receiver. You reconnect a few leads to make the changeover.

If monitoring is done only occasionally in the automobile, the quickest power source is the cigarette lighter socket. Your receiver will either come with a suitable plug, or one may be purchased (Fig. 10-4). If you wire your own plug, be certain that correct polarity is observed. A red power lead from the receiver usually signifies a positive (+) connection and this should connect to the tip or center of the plug. The negative (−) connection should go to the shell or side terminal of the plug.

A permanent installation is accomplished by connecting directly into the electrical system of the car. If your car has a fuse block, chances are that the manufacturer provides extra positions for future accessories. (This may be described in the car owner's manual.) Such circuits often have current ratings of several amperes, enough for almost any monitoring receiver. Most sets draw less than one ampere.

Another point for picking up power is at the rear of the ignition switch. The correct terminal to choose depends on the type of operation you desire. One ideal arrangement allows you to listen to the radio when the ignition is "on" (engine running) or when the ignition key is in the "accessory" position (the engine is off). When the key is removed from the ignition lock, power to the radio is off, even if the set is turned on. Thus, it is nearly impossible to discharge the car battery if you forget to turn off the radio. For this kind of operation, find the terminal on the rear of the ignition switch which controls the accessory power—usually the longest screw on the rear of the switch. Loosen the nut and connect the "hot" lead from the receiver.

If you want to listen to the receiver when the key is removed from the ignition lock, locate the "hot" terminal on the rear of the ignition switch. This can be found by touching the receiver power lead to each of the rear ignition terminals to determine which allows the radio to operate with the key removed. During this test, the receiver must also be grounded.

The receiver is usually grounded when it is mounted. There should be enough mounting hardware touching the car body (or dashboard) to complete the ground circuit.

Fig. 10-4. Power plug for use in cigarette lighter socket.

When the coaxial cable from the antenna is plugged into the receiver, this also establishes a ground (since the cable is grounded at the antenna base). If there is any doubt about the ground, you can run a No. 18 stranded cable from the receiver chassis to the nearest ground point.

CONVERTER INSTALLATION

Converters are easy to install because they are small and can operate from the regular car antenna. Some converters have an internal battery, but certain models must be connected to a 12-volt dc source. Since converters draw so little current (usually just a few milliamperes), you can lift one side of a fuse in the fuse block and insert a lead from the converter between the clip and the fuse. When the fuse is pressed back into place, the wire makes contact. This should be at the fuse which supplies the regular car radio. Connect the wire to the side of the fuse which goes to the radio, not to the power source. You will provide fuse protection if a short circuit develops in the converter, especially in those models which have no built-in fuse.

Locating and mounting a converter follows the techniques already described in some detail. However, you may have to consider cable lengths. A converter may be supplied with a short length of coaxial cable which should not be cut. These cables are of special low-capacity design and cannot be easily spliced. If you must have additional length to make an installation, the converter manufacturer might offer an extension for the purpose. The original length should reach from the converter to the rear of the car radio in most cases.

The cable hookup can be done in a few moments. The manufacturer provides instructions, but the procedure is relatively standard, as detailed in an earlier chapter. However, avoid pulling out speaker plugs and other connections to the radio. One way to be sure you are grasping the correct plug is to check to see whether it connects to a heavy coaxial cable (which runs to the car antenna). This antenna plug is inserted into a matching socket on the converter, often labeled "ANTENNA." The converter has a cable which runs to the radio and inserts into the hole where you pulled out the antenna plug.

Fig. 10-5. Pushbutton is set for 1500-kHz output from converter.

Converters usually have an output signal which is on the upper portion of the a-m broadcast band, 1500 kHz, for example. If you turn on the radio and switch on the converter, you should be able to find the correct setting by hearing incoming signals or a rise in the noise level of the radio. Be sure you are on the frequency recommended by the manufacturer, since there will be hisses or squeals in other portions of the broadcast band. These are spurious responses and do not produce the most sensitive reception. One way to be sure that you are tuning the a-m radio correctly is to set up one pushbutton for converter operation (Fig. 10-5). Any time you wish to listen, simply push that button and turn on the converter.

The pushbutton method is often recommended, but it has some drawbacks. First, it eliminates one pushbutton for regular listening on the a-m band. Second, the pushbutton is not always precise enough to produce perfect converter reception, so you have to do some fine tuning with the a-m radio dial. One way to avoid these problems is to set the pushbutton on the extreme right to the highest a-m station you want to hear. After the converter is turned on, push that button, then *manually* tune the rest of the way to locate the converter signal. With a little practice this can be done very quickly, without giving up one a-m pushbutton.

CONVERTER ANTENNAS

Sharing the antenna with the car radio is one of the conveniences of a converter. A regular a-m whip antenna, how-

Fig. 10-6. Adjusting a-m whip antenna
for converter reception.

ever, may not provide the most sensitivity. One solution is
to adjust the length of the antenna to favor the higher
monitoring frequencies. This is done experimentally by
shortening the antenna for high-band signals, and extend-
ing it to full length for low-band reception. The problem
introduced by this technique is that best reception on high-
band frequencies may occur with the whip length less than
two feet. As a result, reception on the a-m broadcast band
may suffer on weaker signals between towns. Whip adjustment as shown in Fig. 10-6, therefore, is a compromise.

An important final step for any converter installation is
to adjust the antenna trimmer on the a-m radio. Unless this
is done, a-m reception might deteriorate badly after adding
the converter. It is done by locating the trimmer adjustment, which is usually found in one of two positions. In
many cars, it is next to the antenna socket on the a-m radio
(where the antenna cable was unplugged earlier). You can

find it by grasping the cable between two fingers and moving your hand toward the rear of the radio where the plug is inserted. Feel around that point for an opening which contains a screwhead. Try to confirm this by looking under the dashboard with a flashlight. Insert a small screwdriver into the slot (the trimmer) and adjust for best volume on the a-m radio while tuned to a weak station at the high end of the band. Perform this adjustment very carefully; it greatly affects a-m reception sensitivity. The second trimmer type is much easier to adjust. It is accessible from the front of the radio by removing a tuning knob, usually at the right end of the dial as you face the radio, as shown in Fig. 10-7.

ANTENNA
TRIMMER

Fig. 10-7. Location of antenna trimmer in some auto radios.

ANTENNA MOUNTING

When installing a complete monitor receiver, which operates independently of the car radio, you can use the existing a-m antenna. Most receiver manufacturers, however, do not provide the convenient changeover switch that is in the converters. It is assumed that the monitor receiver will operate from a separate antenna. Yet, it is still possible to share the a-m antenna by constructing the switching system shown in Fig. 10-8. It can be made in a small metal box and fitted with the proper sockets (Motorola-type chassis-mount sockets) and a single-pole, double-throw slide switch. You throw the switch each time you go from one receiver to the other.

There is a disadvantage in this system. Although you save one antenna, you sacrifice one receiver while the other

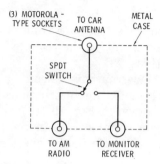

Fig. 10-8. Antenna change-over switch for mobile monitor.

is in operation. This could prove annoying when you wish to monitor during long periods and listen to the a-m radio at the same time. This is solved by another approach to sharing one antenna between two receivers. It is the antenna with a built-in coupling device as shown in Chapter 8. No switching is required since a coil divides and directs the signals to the proper receivers.

The ultimate approach is a separate antenna, tuned specifically to the desired band, mounted on the automobile. The disadvantages are the cost of an additional antenna, plus the need for drilling another hole in the car body for some antenna models. The location on the car depends on the physical size of the antenna. In the high band, antenna lengths of less than two feet are usual, and the ideal location is in the center of the car roof. Since the center of the car roof can present a difficult installation, you might locate the antenna on the side cowl opposite the regular whip antenna. Another location is on the rear deck to the right

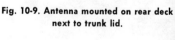

Fig. 10-9. Antenna mounted on rear deck next to trunk lid.

or left of the trunk lid (Fig. 10-9). Low-band antennas, about six-feet long (unless shortened by loading coils), usually mount on the rear deck in professional two-way installations.

Once you have selected a location, study the manufacturer's mounting instructions. A typical mounting procedure is shown in Fig. 10-10. The critical part of the job is drilling a suitable hole in the car body. Be sure to hammer a small dimple in the sheet metal before drilling to prevent

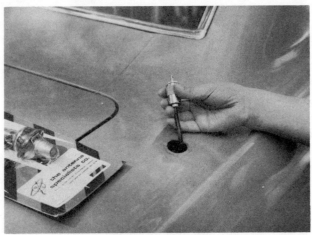

(A) Hole drilled for antenna.

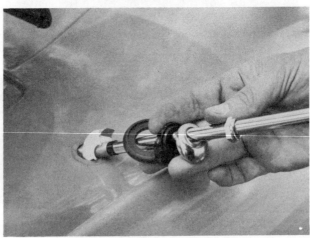

(B) Mounting hardware in place.

Fig. 10-10. Typical installation procedure

marring the finish. An excellent way to enlarge the drill hole to final size is with a chassis punch. This is a circular tool that cuts a neat hole with no danger of slipping or marring the car finish.

ROUTING CABLES

When an antenna is mounted on the rear of a vehicle, the coaxial cable is routed forward from the trunk area into the passenger compartment. To find a passage between these areas, insert a stiff wire (coat hanger, for example) through one of the lower corners of the trunk. It is usually possible to snake a wire from the trunk through a small opening under the rear seat. Once the cable is pulled through, it is routed forward by loosening the screws which hold down the metal molding along the sides of the car floor. This allows the cable to be stuffed under the mat or carpet and routed up behind the dashboard for connection to the receiver. Try to keep the cable away from any areas where it would be subject to excessive abrasion or strain.

Routing the cable from a roof-top antenna calls for some special techniques. One method is to remove the dome light to gain access to the underside of an antenna hole drilled in the roof. Then, route the cable under the headliner.

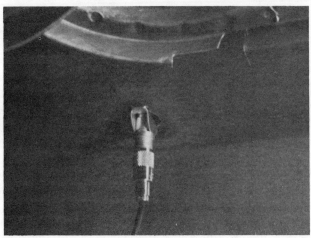

(C) Cable attached to antenna.

for antenna mounted on rear deck.

11

Getting the Most
Out of Equipment

Once your equipment is in operation, you may discover room for improvement. Perhaps you can increase listening range with a better antenna, or move an existing antenna to a better location. Noise and interference could be ruining reception. Also, frequencies change and you no longer hear the stations you want. Let us look at areas of possible change, and what you can do about them.

Some of these steps are extremely simple. Look at the receiver shown in Fig. 11-1, for example. It is a tunable receiver with only approximate dial calibration. A small strip of tape added below the dial provides a marking scale. Whenever you hear a desired station on the band, mark its position with an ink dot. If the signal is of special interest (a local police or fire department, etc.) add identifying letters like "PD." You will not have the accuracy of crystal control, but the dial marking enables you to locate a frequency without actually hearing a signal on the air. One tip on using this system: Always view the dial pointer and ink dot in direct line of sight. Otherwise, you will not be able to repeat the correct setting each time because of parallax, which is a misleading angle formed between the dial and the marking.

INSTALLING CRYSTALS

In a crystal-controlled monitor, changing frequency or adding channels is done by plugging the proper crystal in a socket. The socket may be located either on the outside of the cabinet or may be accessible after removing a panel. Some manufacturers supply no detailed crystal information and require that new crystals be ordered directly from them. You must supply the exact frequency (or channel) of operation down to the last digit—like 46.42 MHz, or 150.995 MHz, for example. If you cannot learn the frequencies through local sources, check with the directories available for this purpose.

A manufacturer often places some limitation on the spacing between crystal frequencies. He might specify a maximum number of megahertz allowed between channels. If the figure is 8 MHz, you would not pick 150 and 161 MHz, for example, because they are too far apart. In actual operation, if such spacing is selected, the receiver would probably operate on strong local signals. Excessive spacing causes a drop in sensitivity to below the manufacturer's specifications. But you might be willing to accept this sacrifice in performance to obtain reception on widely spaced local signals.

Crystal spacing might also be stated as a percentage of the operating frequency. If the value "10 percent" is used, it means a receiver operating on, say, 40 MHz could have a second frequency as far as 4 MHz above or below 40 MHz.

On a higher band, the percentage may drop to only 4 percent of the operating frequency. In some models, the manufacturer will make available a special crystal to reduce interference when a strong station operates adjacent to the one you wish to hear. These special crystals are manufactured to very close tolerances and allow the receiver to be tuned farther away from the interfering signal, but remain within its allotted slot (frequency tolerance) and receive the desired channel.

Other manufacturers provide the necessary information to order a crystal from a crystal manufacturer. The instruction manual contains a formula plus electrical data on the crystal. For example, let us say you want to equip a monitor with a crystal for 162.550 MHz (the continuous weather service on the high band). A typical formula:

Crystal Frequency (MHz) =

$$\frac{\text{Receiving Frequency} - 10.7 \text{ MHz}}{3}$$

For 162.550 MHz this becomes:

$$\text{Crystal Frequency} = \frac{162.550 - 10.7}{3}$$

$$= \frac{151.850}{3}$$

$$= 50.6166 \text{ MHz}$$

You would, therefore, order a 50.6166 MHz crystal to receive 162.550 MHz. The 10.7 MHz figure in the formula is supplied by the manufacturer. It is the intermediate frequency (i-f) of the receiver and remains constant.

The instruction manual furnished with the receiver will also give additional information you must know to order the correct crystal, including holder type, load capacity, and mode. For example, the specifications of a typical receiver are:

Holder type: HC-18U
Load capacitance: 32 pF
Mode: Third overtone, parallel resonance
Frequency tolerance: .0025% at 25 degrees C.

If any other data is given, such as drive level and resistance, include it in the ordering information.

ELECTRICAL INTERFERENCE

One of the benefits of reception above 30 MHz is high immunity to certain types of interference. Static, hiss, and buzz caused by arcing in rotating machinery tends to be reduced at higher frequencies. An appliance which disrupts reception on a conventional short-wave receiver, for example, may produce no audible effect on a vhf set. In monitoring various bands, you may discover that automobiles passing on a nearby street may disrupt reception on the low band, but produce little effect on the high band. The ignition noise causing the interference cannot reach completely across the radio spectrum. But since all bands are susceptible to at least some electrical interference, there are methods to reduce or eliminate it completely.

Interference in a home monitoring receiver arises from a collection of atmospheric and man-made sources. The general rule is that the stronger the incoming signal, the more the receiver can resist such interference. Thus, a good starting point in any fight against interference is to secure the best possible antenna system and mount it in a high location. As the circuit receives a stronger signal, it automatically reduces reception sensitivity and becomes more immune to noise.

A good ground may also improve reception. This is usually done by installing a heavy wire (No. 18 or larger) between the chassis (or the ground terminal at the antenna connection) and the electrical ground of the building. A building ground is often at a cold water pipe and, in many cases, at the screw which holds the cover plate on an ac outlet (Fig. 11-2). If a coaxial line runs outdoors, you may peel away part of the plastic jacket to expose the shield. It can be grounded to an outdoor pipe by wrapping and soldering a heavy wire to the shield and connecting it to the electrical ground (Fig. 11-3).

Home appliances are generators of electrical noise. If the source is obviously a vacuum cleaner, electric razor, or mixer, it is rarely worth any treatment since these appli-

Fig. 11-2. Connecting ground wire to ac-outlet cover screw.

ances are operated only at brief intervals. But if the source is the ignition system of an oil burner, for example, it can prove troublesome. The cure is to place the antenna as far as possible from the burner and to use a coaxial cable. The cable can shield against interference pickup (Fig. 11-4), especially in areas close to the source.

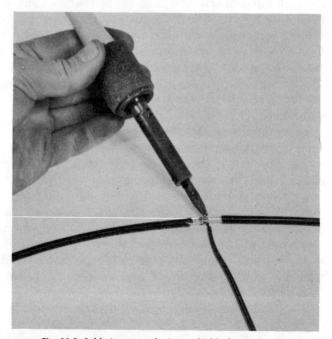

Fig. 11-3. Soldering ground wire to shield of coaxial cable.

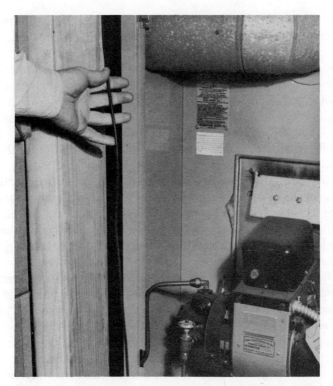

Fig. 11-4. Coaxial antenna cable used near oil burner.

TV sets are prolific noise generators. Most interference occurs from the horizontal deflection system which creates sharp pulses rich in harmonic radiation. It contains signals which extend into the vhf region and are heard in the receiver as a rough-sounding buzz. The noise often drops in and out as you tune across a band, since the offending sig-

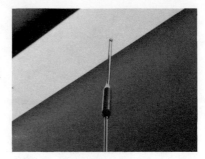

Fig. 11-5. Keep receiver antenna away from fluorescent lamp.

nals appear at regular points along the dial. The cure is to keep the receiver as far as possible from the TV set. Merely moving the receiver several feet away may be enough to solve the problem. Remember, too, that radiation travels through solid walls and may carry interference to adjoining rooms.

Lighting appliances are possible interference sources. One frequent culprit is the fluorescent lamp (Fig. 11-5), which produces sharp electrical pulses (similar to those created by the TV set). Space the receiver and antenna as far as possible from the source if you discover any link between lighting and radio noise. Far less common is radio interference from a regular filament-type electric lamp. You can detect this type of interference if you hear any crackling in the receiver that disappears when a lamp is turned off. It is cured by replacing the noisy lamp.

Electrical line filters are sold for reducing appliance noises. The simplest type is a bypass capacitor enclosed in an ac socket, while more elaborate units contain coils. These filters are of limited value since they only affect noise impressed on the line carrying ac house current. They cannot be effective on airborne noise (radiation) which reaches the antenna system directly. In severe cases, it may prove helpful to install a line filter at the interference source—a fan, for example. If you have some technical knowledge, first try bypassing the interference to ground inside the appliance or fixture. One effective method is to connect a .01 μF disc capacitor, rated at 600 volts dc or more, across the ac wires inside the appliance (Fig. 11-6). The bare wires should be carefully soldered and taped to prevent possible short circuits. If the appliance is a permanent

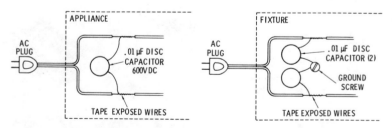

Fig. 11-6. Installing bypass capacitor inside electrical appliance.

Fig. 11-7. Installing bypass capacitors in permanently grounded appliance.

fixture, which has an electrically grounded metal body, use two such capacitors. Connect one side of each capacitor to each side of the ac line. The other side of each capacitor is connected to electrical ground, as shown in Fig. 11-7.

Also, try the ac plug from the receiver both ways in the outlet. Select the position that produces the least interference.

MOBILE NOISE

The greatest offender in the automobile is the spark plug. It generates electrical radiation rich in interference. One way to avoid this is to change to resistor-type spark plugs. Another method is to replace the high-tension cables between the plugs, the ignition coil, and the distributor with the resistance-type cable. Before trying it, though, check to see whether the manufacturer has already installed this type cable, as is the case in most late-model cars. Do not use *both* resistor spark plugs and resistance cable, or your engine timing might be disturbed.

Auto manufacturers usually provide some devices for suppressing noise in the car radio. Their measures, however, may not be effective for the higher frequencies encountered in two-way radio. To silence a noisy generator, you should use special coaxial capacitors made for the purpose. The generator noise is treated by a .5 μF coaxial capacitor connected to the "A" (armature) terminal. It should cure the musical whine that rises and falls with engine speed. If the car has an alternator instead of a generator, the whining noise is usually caused by dirty slip rings or faulty diodes. Have the rings cleaned or the diodes replaced, and you are ready for quieter reception.

12

Building a Sensitive Antenna

There is always an elusive, enticing signal just over the horizon that cannot be heard with a standard antenna. You might make out a word or two on certain days when the weather (which affects both uhf and vhf) or some other variable element improves the transmission path. Or you may tune to some frequency on the receiver and see the S-meter indicator move slightly. You may hear a reduction in background noise, but still be unable to "copy" the audio. Don't despair. By utilizing the techniques used by communications engineers in the design of two-way antennas, you can multiply the energy of a feeble signal several times. It is sometimes possible to lift station signals out of the noise level to a listenable status.

This is done by building "gain" into the antenna system. Although the word implies amplification, antenna gain is actually achieved by introducing additional elements to intercept more of the available signal. The gain, however, is achieved at some expense to the directionality of the antenna. You will be able to pick up weaker signals, but from a narrower arc. Hams, TV viewers, and others overcome this disadvantage by using a mast-mounted rotator to point the antenna toward the signal source. It is also possible for the antenna to remain fixed in the desired direction, or be manually rotated if the bottom of the mast is within reach.

This is practical if the antenna is indoors (in the listening room, for example).

HORIZONTAL AND VERTICAL MOUNTING

Since most signals arrive from cruising mobile stations, two-way radio systems usually use antennas which are *vertically* polarized. Vertical antennas are easier to operate in a nondirectional mode. The antenna described in this chapter can be operated in either horizontal or vertical polarization simply by changing the physical mounting, as we will see. If you use the horizontally mounted antenna to hear vertically polarized signals, there might be a partial signal loss due to "cross polarization." One factor, however, might offset this disadvantage—a horizontal antenna might work better in an electrically noisy location since man-made interference is less prevalent in the horizontal plane. In any case, antennas for vhf and uhf are physically small and easy to mount either way, so you can experiment with both positions. Vhf signals often bounce and lose their original polarization, especially over long distances.

THE TYPICAL BEAM

The sensitive antenna described below grew out of a need to hear a station only 16 miles away. Although the distance seems short, the station is not intended for normal reception. It transmits from an airport as a navigational aid for aircraft. The station operates at very low power and is rated for reliable reception up to 25 miles, meaning it is limited to the antennas mounted on flying aircraft. In a home receiver, the signal could be identified only by a slight drop in receiver hiss as the dial swept past the frequency. The *beam* antenna in Fig. 12-1, especially designed for that frequency, vastly boosted the signal and permitted successful reception.

You can construct a similar antenna for almost any frequency you wish to hear. The basic design is that of a three-element Yagi consisting of a director, a reflector, and a driven element. By cutting the rods to certain lengths, the antenna becomes extremely responsive to the desired signal.

Fig. 12-1. Three-element beam antenna.

HOMEMADE BEAM

Before looking at the final model, you might first consider a stripped-down version that could solve some weak-signal reception problems. The antenna shown in Fig. 12-2 is a *half-wave dipole* cut to the operating frequency. Such an antenna displays a bidirectional pattern in that the best sensitivity occurs when the element is broadside to the station. To make the dipole, follow the plan shown in Fig. 12-2. It is handy to construct the elements from wire or from aluminum tubing widely available in local hardware stores. Note that the overall span of the elements is given as one-half wavelength, with a break in the middle. Although the exact width of the opening is not important, keep the tubing ends far enough apart so that dirt or moisture cannot easily form a bridge across the gap. This is especially important if you are mounting the antenna outdoors.

An actual model is shown being constructed in Fig. 12-3. Note that the ends of the tubing (the center of the antenna)

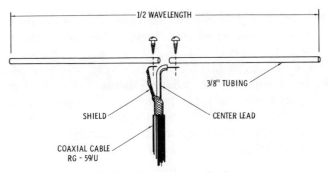

Fig. 12-2. Basic half-wave dipole.

are held in place by wood screws driven through holes drilled in the elements and into the wood support or "boom" which is made from 1-inch square stock. The coaxiable cable is the kind sold for TV lead-in and has a rated impedance of approximately 72 ohms (RG-59/U). Some solder lugs placed under the screws enable you to fasten the shield and center lead of the coaxial cable to the center of the split element.

Fig. 12-3. Constructing a half-wave dipole.

This simple dipole can outperform the whip antenna on the receiver, even when the dipole is located in the room. A great advantage is that the dipole may be moved about the room independently of the receiver; this is useful in capturing bouncing vhf and uhf waves. Once you locate a "hot" spot, fasten or tape the antenna in some permanent arrangement. Next, let us consider how to figure that half-wavelength dimension for tuning the dipole to a frequency you want to hear.

CALCULATING THE HALF-WAVELENGTH ELEMENT

A simple formula solves the half-wavelength question. Simply *divide* 468 by the desired frequency (in Megahertz). The answer will be the length of a half wave in *feet*. For example, here is how we found the element length for 113 MHz, the frequency of the antennas shown in the photos:

$$\text{Half wave (in feet)} = \frac{468}{113}$$

$$= 4.14 \text{ feet}$$

We will drop the fraction and use a practical length of 4 feet, or 48 inches, for the half wave of the operating frequency. This represents the *overall* length of the dipole measured from the outside ends. If you want to cut a dipole to a *band* of frequencies, rather than to a single value, choose the center frequency of the group and base your calculation on this figure. Although a dipole favors a narrow range, it should perform reasonably well within about 20 percent of the center frequency. (This would be more critical if the antenna served for transmission, as well as for reception.)

In mounting the dipole, try the elements in both horizontal and vertical positions for best results. If you mount the dipole vertically, bring the coaxial cable away from the elements at a right angle for several feet, since the cable may interfere with antenna action if it is allowed to drop down next to the lower element.

ADDING ELEMENTS

Much greater antenna sensitivity is possible with the full-size, three-element beam. As shown in Fig. 12-4, the original dipole is now termed the "driven" element and remains the same size as determined by the half-wave formula. A second element, termed the "director," is positioned in front of the driven element (where it is first to intercept the arriving signal). The third element, the "reflector," is behind the driven element at the rear of the array. With this arrangement, far more signal is collected and the resulting energy is concentrated in the driven element, which feeds the coaxial line down to the receiver.

With the aid of the half-wave formula and the additional dimensions given in Fig. 12-4, you should be able to design a practical beam for almost any frequency. The starting point is always the half-wave dipole, or driven element, at the center position. Once you have determined that length (as already described), it is a simple matter to cut the driven element to the correct length. Notice in Fig. 12-4 that the director is labeled "−5%," which means that it is five percent *shorter* than the driven element. The reflector element, marked "+5%" is cut five percent *longer* than the driven element. Let us return to the practical example and see how the actual element lengths are based on these values.

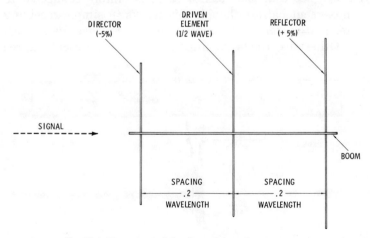

Fig. 12-4. Dimensions of the three-element beam antenna.

Our working model was constructed for a frequency of 113 MHz, and the half-wave dipole was calculated at 48 inches. This becomes the driven element dimension. Since the director is 5 percent shorter, we will cut it to a length 2.4 (48 × .05) inches shorter than the driven element, or 45.6 inches. Determining reflector length is even simpler because we merely add 2.4 inches (5 percent) to the driven element dimension. The reflector is cut to a length of 50.4 inches. We now have the three elements, and we need one further dimension: the spacing between them. If you check the basic beam shown in Fig. 12-4, you will see an element spacing of 0.2 wavelength. Watch out for a possible error in this calculation since it is based on a *full*, not a half, wavelength. Just double the half wave—from 48 to 96 inches, in our example—and multiply it by 0.2. The correct spacing is 19.2 (96 × 0.2) inches. With this simple arithmetic (and a thanks to Dr. Hidetsugu Yagi, the inventor), you can build one of the most efficient antennas ever conceived.

GAMMA MATCH

There is one more device to consider in the construction of the beam antenna. If you refer back to the basic half-wave dipole antenna described at the outset of this chapter, you will see that the coaxial cable is simply connected to each element half. Although this works in simple receiving systems, it is worth a bit more effort to improve the connection. Otherwise, the beam antenna does not electrically agree

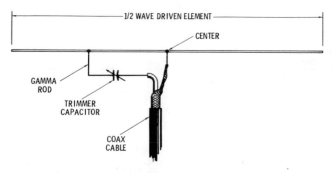

Fig. 12-5. Gamma-match antenna connection.

with the coaxial cable serving as the feedline to the receiver. To improve the connection, we will use a *gamma match,* a device which enables you to adjust the line to the antenna and improve the signal transfer. As shown in Fig. 12-5, the shield of the coaxial cable connects to the center of the driven element. An important difference between this hookup and the one in the simpler dipole mentioned earlier is that the driven element is now a continuous, *unbroken* length. The center lead of the coaxial cable connects through a variable capacitor to a tap-in point on the element.

CONSTRUCTION

Let us put the formulas to work and build a practical antenna. Do *not* use the dimensions given in the example unless you also want to receive the center of the aviation navigational band. Just perform the same calculations to come up with all the values for other frequencies. The same construction techniques, however, can serve for any band.

The three-element antenna illustrated in the photos proved highly successful in operation. Before it was built, a "rabbit-ear" indoor TV antenna was used to pick up the vhf signals with only moderate success. After orienting the "rabbit-ear" antenna, the signal would barely rise above the noise level. The beam antenna, even indoors, more than triples the amount of signal power delivered to the receiver. Reception on the desired channel is noise-free, and signals once buried in the background noise are readable. When the antenna was mounted outdoors, reception improved even further.

Now we will concentrate on the practical construction details shown in Fig. 12-6. The boom that supports the three elements is a length of 1-inch square wood stock drilled with $\frac{3}{8}$-inch holes to receive the three aluminum tubes (Fig. 12-7). You may have to lightly tap the tubes through the drill holes, but this also secures them to the boom by friction. When the elements are positioned, do not hide their centerlines inside the wood boom. The centers should line up next to the wood boom to allow the cable shield to be fastened to the center of the driven element. A 6-32 bolt and nut, plus a solder lug, can be used for this connection.

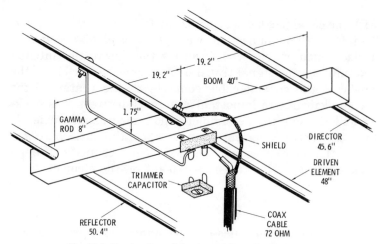

Fig. 12-6. Construction of the three-element beam antenna.

The center lead of the coaxial cable connects to one lug of a terminal strip, which also supports one side of a mica compression-type trimmer capacitor. The value of the trimmer capacitor should be approximately 100 pF in the maxi-

Fig. 12-7. Installing aluminum element in the boom.

mum capacity position. The other side of the capacitor is soldered to the same lug that receives the gamma rod (Fig. 12-8). The rod is made from a length of solid wire and should be spaced about 1½ inches from the driven element. The length of the gamma rod depends on the length of the driven element. It should extend about one-third the distance from the boom to the end of the driven element. The gamma rod shown is 8-inches long, since half the driven element is 24 inches. The gamma rod is secured at its extreme end by a 6-32 nut and bolt through the driven element.

The antenna is fastened to a mast by two holes drilled in the boom to receive a U-bolt (Fig. 12-9). You can devise other ways to support the antenna if it is to be used indoors. (For example, the boom may be suspended from an attic ceiling by cord.) If the antenna will be subject to the weather, some additional treatment is in order. The wood boom should receive several coats of varnish to prevent moisture from causing deterioration. Also, you will have

Fig. 12-8. The gamma rod.

Fig. 12-9. The antenna mounted on the mast.

Fig. 12-10. Adjusting the trimmer capacitor.

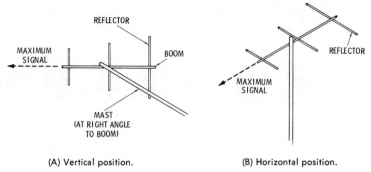

(A) Vertical position.   (B) Horizontal position.

Fig. 12-11. Mounting positions for the beam.

to provide some method for keeping the trimmer capacitor and terminal strip dry during wet weather or from becoming short-circuited by soot deposits. A plastic box cut to fit over the trimmer assembly or plastic tape should solve these problems.

TUNING THE BEAM

It is easiest to tune the antenna if you have access to a steady signal source, such as an rf signal generator, and some method for reading signal strength (an S-meter or an ac voltmeter connected to the speaker leads). In the absence of these instruments, you can still tune the antenna by listening to an on-the-air station. Place the antenna array somewhere in the room where the elements are at least their own length away from nearby metal. While listening to the signal, try to improve its strength by adjusting the trimmer with a nonmetallic screwdriver or alignment tool (Fig. 12-10). You may have to swing the antenna toward the station in order to be sure that you have the correct tuning adjustment. Once this is done, it should not be necessary to retune the antenna each time you dial to a new station in the band. After tuning, mount the antenna in the horizontal or vertical plane (Fig. 12-11), depending on which polarization produces the best results. Also, avoid placing the antenna closer than one-half wavelength (the dimension of the driven element) from any nearby metal in order to prevent distortion to the pickup pattern.

Index